D1131319

Romping Through Mathematics

Other Borzoi Books for Young People

HURRICANES AND TWISTERS by *Robert Irving*

THE MIGHTY ATOM by *John Lewellen*

MODEL RAILROADING by *Harry Zarchy*

CERAMICS by *Harry Zarchy*

LET'S MAKE SOMETHING by *Harry Zarchy*

Published by Alfred A. Knopf

Romping Through Mathematics

By RAYMOND W. ANDERSON

Illustrated by *HARRY ZARCHY*

NEW YORK *Alfred A Knopf*

1956

GOSHEN COLLEGE LIBRARY
GOSHEN, INDIANA

Juv.
QA
36
A6

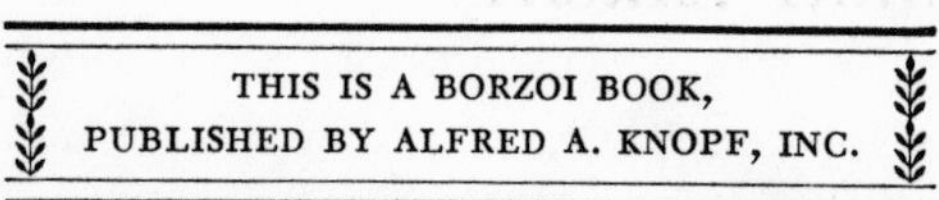

THIS IS A BORZOI BOOK,
PUBLISHED BY ALFRED A. KNOPF, INC.

Copyright 1947 *by Alfred A. Knopf, Inc. All rights reserved. No part of this book may be reproduced in any form without permission in writing from the publisher, except by a reviewer who may quote brief passages or reproduce not more than three illustrations in a review to be printed in a magazine or newspaper. Manufactured in the United States of America. Published in Canada by McClelland & Stewart Limited.*

Published August 21, 1947. Second printing, March 1948. Third printing, January 1951. Fourth printing, November 1953. Fifth printing, April 1956.

Note

MATHEMATICS *is the science of learning how to count and measure. It is one of the oldest if not* the *oldest of the sciences; it is so old that its name doesn't even mean "to count and measure," but "to learn." The ancient Greeks used the word* manthano *which means "to learn." For at least four thousand years men and women have been learning how to count and measure.* ROMPING THROUGH MATHEMATICS *is the story of how, during those four thousand years, the necessary mental tools for counting and measuring were collected and arranged.*

R. W. A.

Romping Through Mathematics

To Ella and Leigh,
Michael and John;
Who'll romp through math
And soon catch on.

As Easy as One, Two, Three

ARITHMETIC

ARITHMETIC is the science of numbers just as botany is the science of plants and astronomy the science of the stars. Even in the very early days of recorded history men knew something about numbers. They had to. They had to count their children or their sheep or their arrows. It all came rather easily.

"Why it's as easy as one . . . two . . . three!" How often you hear that said. The idea of picking up one apple, then another apple, and then another apple and stating that there are *three* apples is very simple.

The Chinese said *san* for three; the Babylonians *sălăsu;* the Egyptians *xemet;* the Greeks *gamma;* the Romans *tres;* the Arabs *talāta;* the French *trois;* and of course in English we use the word *three.*

When people stopped *talking* about three apples and began to write down signs for numbers, what differences appeared! This is the way the Greeks and Romans, for example, expressed them.

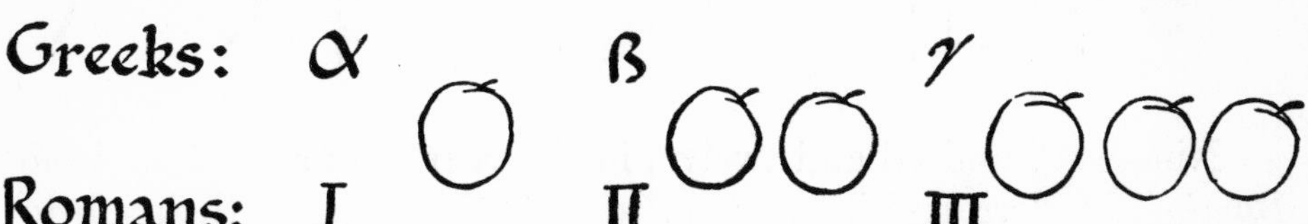

Greeks: α β γ

Romans: I II III

But the Arabs were much cleverer than the Greeks or the Romans in the science of numbers. In fact, some unknown Arabian genius invented such good signs for numbers that almost all the people in the world today have adopted the Arabic invention and discarded their own ancestors' clumsy scratches used as number words.

To be sure, all of us still have to learn two sets of numbers, the Roman and the Arabic. We need to know Roman numbers in order to read the faces of clocks or the inscriptions on cornerstones, like the one inscribed on a certain school which was built *Anno Domini* M C M X I I.

The first "M" of course stands for one thousand. The second "M" would naturally stand for another thousand except that the placing of the "C" before the "M" indicates that one hundred is to be subtracted. The only reason for this is that the Romans did it that way. So MCM stands for nineteen hundred. The "X" is ten, plus "I" makes eleven and another "I" makes twelve.

Nineteen hundred and twelve, in the year of our Lord or *Anno Domini!* Modern architects seem to make it a part of their job to keep alive the clumsy old Roman numbers.

We must admit that architects, as well as watchmakers — not to mention doctors and druggists who go completely Roman when they mysteriously write III ounces of castor oil — certainly do stick to tradition.

But back in their own offices, when they are figuring as to how many bricks or tons of steel they are going to need for the new school which they are building, do architects go through any such performance as this?

NUMBER OF BRICKS REQUIRED

For the West Wall....................	M M M M M M M
For the North Wall....................	M M M M M M
For the East Wall....................	M M M M M M M
For the South Wall....................	M M M M M
Total MMMMMMMMMM MMMMMMMMMM MMMMM	

Not for a single second does Mr. Architect have anything to do with the ancient Romans and their clumsy figures. Instead he trots out the new-fangled Arabic invention, and this is how he figures out his order for bricks:

1234567890

Arabian Patent #654907

NUMBER OF BRICKS REQUIRED

For the West Wall..........................	7,000
For the North Wall..........................	6,000
For the East Wall..........................	7,000
For the South Wall..........................	5,000
Total..................................	25,000

Adding and subtracting have been done in pretty much the same way by all peoples in all places in all times, especially when only small numbers were involved such as computing dates of births and deaths, or the simple counting of fingers and toes. In fact, fingers and toes were used by many peoples as primitive adding machines. Among many uncivilized people the numbers, five, ten, and twenty are important. There are still many people who count on their fingers. To be sure, they don't do it openly; that is, they don't use the "two-handed" method. They catch the answer with one hand. The hand is kept on the seat beside them, or under the other hand on the counter. (Odd, isn't it, that we call a table in a grocery store a "counter!") Then under their breath and hardly moving their lips, they say to themselves, "Six and nine make fifteen . . . and three, eighteen . . . and eleven, twenty-nine. . . ."

It's really all a matter of practice, and what a lot of practice we get, adding up grocery bills and laundry bills and all other sorts of bills and then subtracting them from the family's weekly income!

But when it comes to multiplying and dividing, that is a different story. The multiplication tables we use and the methods for short and long division come directly from our old friends, the Arabs.

Just suppose we continued to use Greek methods. They used their "a-b-c's" for numbers, only of course they called them *alpha, beta, gamma* . . . and so on down to *omega* at the end of the alphabet. We would think that we were using a secret military code instead of the multiplication table.

If 1, 2, 3, 4, and 5 are represented by a, b, c, d, and e, the beginning of the Greek multiplication table must have looked like this:

(1)	a × a = a	a × b = b	a × c = c
(2)	b × a = b	b × b = d	b × c = f
(3)	c × a = c	c × b = f	c × c = i
(4)	d × a = d	d × b = h	d × c = jb
(5)	e × a = e	e × b = j	e × c = je

Yes, all of that trouble to get from 1×1 to 5×3. It makes us appreciate a few of our modern conveniences such as:

$1 \times 1 = 1$	$1 \times 2 = 2$	$1 \times 3 = 3$
$2 \times 1 = 2$	$2 \times 2 = 4$	$2 \times 3 = 6$
$3 \times 1 = 3$	$3 \times 2 = 6$	$3 \times 3 = 9$
$4 \times 1 = 4$	$4 \times 2 = 8$	$4 \times 3 = 12$
$5 \times 1 = 5$	$5 \times 2 = 10$	$5 \times 3 = 15$

Actually, it wasn't until two or three hundred years ago that even the people who went to school had to *learn* the multiplication tables. The tables were like a telephone directory: when you wanted to find out what 11×12 was, you looked it up in the multiplication table which looked like this:

(1)	2	3	4	5	6	7	8	9	10	11	12
2	(4)	6	8	10	12	14	16	18	20	22	24
3	6	(9)	12	15	18	21	24	27	30	33	36
4	8	12	(16)	20	24	28	32	36	40	44	48
5	10	15	20	(25)	30	35	40	45	50	55	60
6	12	18	24	30	(36)	42	48	54	60	66	72
7	14	21	28	35	42	(49)	56	63	70	77	84
8	16	24	32	40	48	56	(64)	72	80	88	96
9	18	27	36	45	54	63	72	(81)	90	99	108
10	20	30	40	50	60	70	80	90	(100)	110	120
11	22	33	44	55	66	77	88	99	110	(121)	132
12	24	36	48	60	72	84	96	108	120	132	(144)

When you wanted to find out how much 7×8 was, for example, you looked across line seven to the eighth column and read off the answer. Of course, after a while it was more trouble to look up the numbers than it was to remember them, and so that is how multiplication tables got into schools. People just decided that, in the long run, it was easier to learn them in the first place.

An interesting diagonal line in the table is marked by parentheses from top left to bottom right. Each of these numbers is the square of the number at the top of its column or the number multiplied by itself, in the 2 column, in the 3 column and so on: 1, 4, 9, 16, 25, 36, 49, 64, 81, 100, 121, and 144. When you multiply 9×9, you get 81; 10×10, 100; 11×11, 121; and so on. This is the same as making a square 9 inches by 9 inches, or 9 feet by 9 feet. But if you have a square and want to find the length of its side, that is quite a different problem.

It is all very simple if you start with a small "perfect" square — that is one you recognize as being in the multiplication table, such as 9 is the perfect square of 3, 144 of 12, etc. But what about one that is much too large to appear in an ordinary multiplication table? And what about a square that is not perfect? Then trouble *really* starts.

Why not make for ourselves a giant multiplication table? It looks like this, and is used in exactly the same way as the ordinary multiplication table with one exception. Many unimportant numbers are left out. But the round number "perfect squares" are all there.

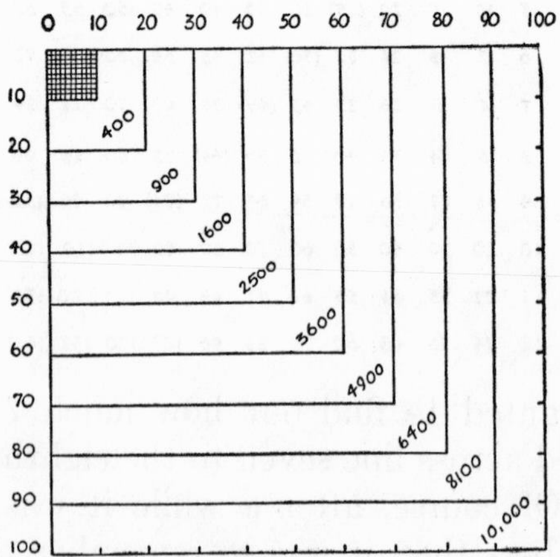

In the upper left hand corner, very much reduced in size, is our old friend, the multiplication table from 1 to 10. We know these perfect squares because we know the multiplication table. We notice that all the numbers from 1 to 9 when squared never need more than two figures (digits) to express the square. Take 9×9, for example. When squared, 9 becomes only 81; only two figures are required to express the square of this single digit.

It takes three or four figures to write down the squares of all the numbers, beginning with 10 and ending with 99. It takes five or six figures to write down the squares of all the numbers beginning with 100 and ending with 999. To put the idea in a nutshell, here's what happens when you square numbers:

1	×	1	=	1
9	×	9	=	81
10	×	10	=	100
99	×	99	=	9,801
100	×	100	=	10,000
999	×	999	=	998,001
1,000	×	1,000	=	1,000,000
9,999	×	9,999	=	99,980,001

When the square of a number consists of one or two digits, the square root of it is always one digit.

When the square of a number consists of three or four digits, the square root of it is always two digits.

When the square of a number consists of five or six digits, the square root of it is always three digits.

When the square of a number consists of seven or eight digits, the square root of it is always four digits, and so on.

So the *first* thing to do when you have a number and want to find its square root is to divide it from right to left into pairs of figures. The rest is really quite simple. Let's take 3,844 for example. The first thing we do is to divide it up into pairs of figures: 38'44. We know by looking at it that the square root will have two figures in it. By looking at the giant multiplication table, we see that 3,844 falls between 3,600 and 4,900. So the square root of 3,844 is somewhere between 60 and 70. The point of interest is: exactly where between 60 and 70?

After taking a look at the giant multiplication table, you would say offhand that a 3,844 square would be considerably nearer to a 3,600 square than to a 4,900 square. In other words, the square root of 3,844 would be considerably nearer to 60 than to 70. Still we come back to the same old point: how near to 60?

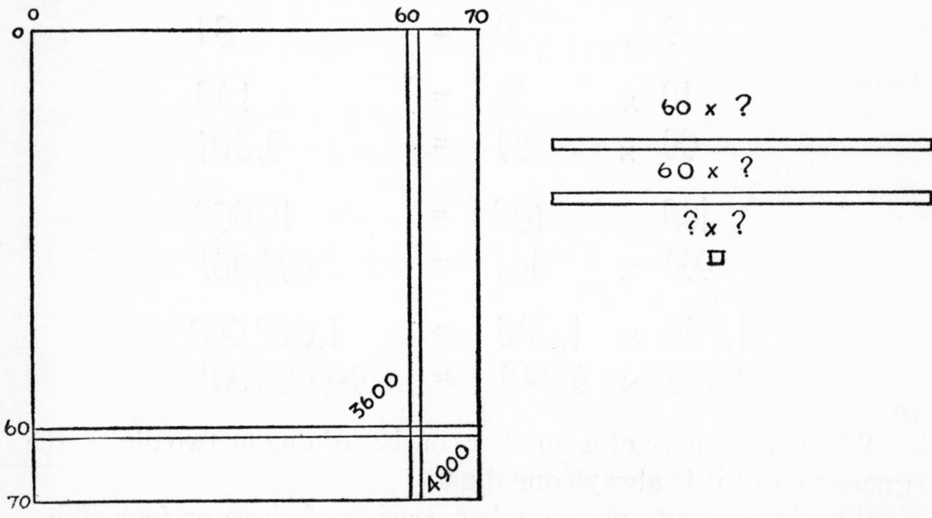

From the multiplication table, we can see that when the 3,600 square (60 × 60) is disposed of, two ribbons and a little square pip are left to represent the 244 (3,844 minus 3,600) which we still have to dispose of. Each ribbon is 60 units long and ? units wide. Together they should make a ribbon 120 units long. (Let's forget the little square for the moment.) Well, how wide can a ribbon 120 units long be if we have only 244 units to work with? Not *much* over 2 units wide. As a matter of fact, if the ribbon *is* 2 units wide, the 240 units are taken care of and the square pip is 2×2; and that takes care of the entire remainder. Our 3,844 unit square has two sides *exactly* 62 units long! And the square root of 3,844 is 62!

By the time this story of the square root gets salted down between the green covers of the usual arithmetic book, it is abbreviated almost beyond recognition. In the early days of printing, type was scarce and paper was expensive. Makers of arithmetic books apparently never have recovered from their early poverty.

Anyway, here's about all you are told, without any synopsis of "That which has happened already":

From right to left, group the figures in pairs.

Beginning at the left, extract the square root. Write it on the answer line. Square the number and subtract from the first pair of figures. (Dizzy?)

Multiply the first figure on the answer line by 20, "bring down" the next pair of figures and see how many times it goes into the pair "brought down."

Put that in the answer line.

Put it in the trial divisor, too. Multiply. Subtract. Start the same thing all over.

"Why?"

"Because it works . . . and you can prove it . . . and because that's the way the square root story generally is explained!"

Maybe you'll prefer to remember the two ribbons and the little square pip.

When it comes to doing *cube* root, perhaps a quick glance at the multiplication table for cubes will give you an idea about marking off groups of three figures in the number to be "un-cubed."

$$1 \times 1 \times 1 = 1$$
$$9 \times 9 \times 9 = 729$$
$$10 \times 10 \times 10 = 1{,}000$$
$$99 \times 99 \times 99 = 970{,}299$$
$$100 \times 100 \times 100 = 1{,}000{,}000$$
$$999 \times 999 \times 999 = 997{,}002{,}999$$

When there are one, two, or three figures in the number, a cube root has only one figure. There are two figures in the cube root when the cube has four, five, or six figures; there are three figures in the cube root when the cube has seven, eight, or nine figures.

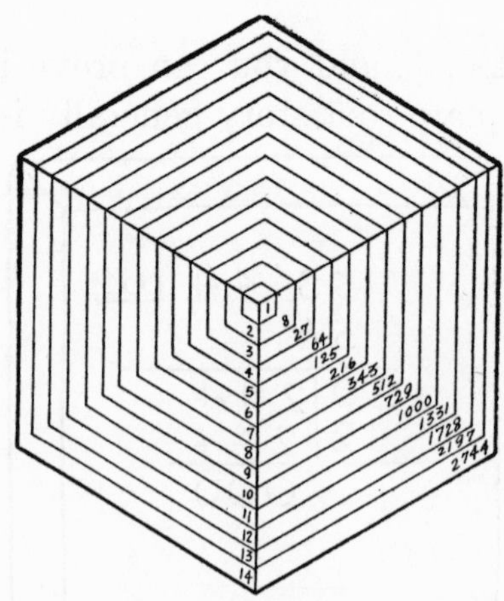

Here is a multiplication table for cubes up to 14. We can see that the cube root changes to a number with two figures in it when the number 1,000 is reached.

Let's try to find the cube root of 10,648. That's quite a bit larger than anything appearing on our multiplication table. Since it has five figures in it, we know that the cube root will have two figures. It is already divided into groups of three figures.

The largest cube that will go into the first group to the left, that is 10, is 2. Since we know that there is to be another figure following that, we are taking out a cube of 20 × 20 × 20 or 8,000. That leaves 10,648 minus 8,000 or 2,648 to dispose of.

Supposing you were told to square 20, multiply by 3, use as a trial divisor. Square the trial quotient and multiply by 20 and by 3. Cube the trial quotient. Mix together, shake well, allow to cool, and just before retiring for the night, subtract from the "taken down" 2,648.

Honestly, now, with that sort of potion inside your head, if in your sleep you should cry out, "Daddy CUBED!" just who could blame you? (Of course Daddy cubed is merely: Daddy, Daddy, Daddy!)

Just why do we do all those things?

Well, in the first place we know that the first large cube we cut out of 10,648 is a 20 × 20 × 20 cube or 8,000. (A 30 × 30 × 30 cube would be too large because it is 27,000.) So-o-o-o . . . we take out our 8,000 cube and then have to dispose of the remainder, 2,648.

Take a look at the 8,000 cube taken out. That's the situation at

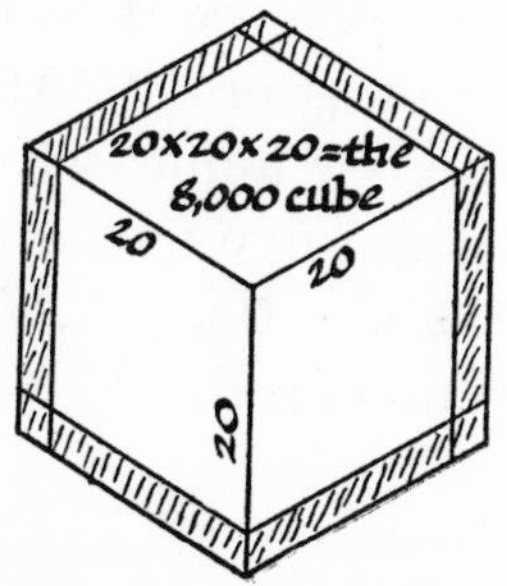

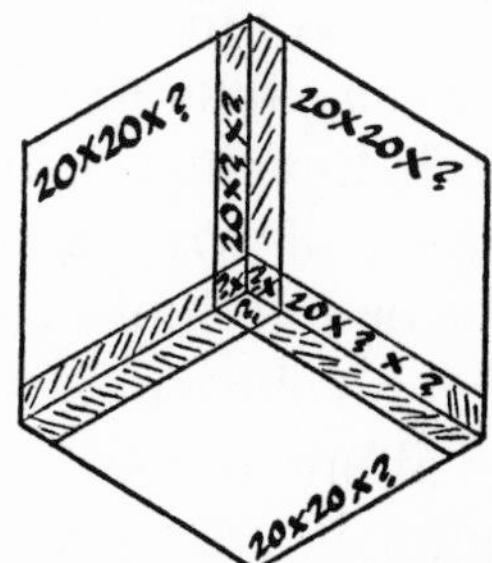

the left. Then turn the problem over and have a look at the under side. That's the situation at the right.

Our remainder is made up of three very sizable chunks, each one $20 \times 20 \times$? The three of them together have a *surface* of 1,200 square units, inches for example. And our remainder is only 2,648 cubic inches. If our chunks were two inches thick, they alone would use up 2,400 cubic inches. But then we have those three long blocks, and each one of them is going to use up $20 \times 2 \times 2$ cubic inches or 80 cubic inches, making 240 cubic inches for the three of them. There remains the little cubic pip, $2 \times 2 \times 2$ or 8 cubic inches. Add them up: 2,400, 240, and 8. The total is 2,648, our entire remainder.

So the cube root of 10,648 is 22; because a 20 inch cube uses up 8,000 cubic inches and the seven remaining pieces make up the rest.

Perhaps it will be a bit easier now to remember why you do all the things you do in extracting cube roots.

You may or may not have noticed that both 3,844 and 10,648 were rather carefully chosen in advance. The square root and the cube root came out in whole numbers. What if something were left over? Then, of course, fractions would appear. And fractions are such bugbears to some people!

There probably are two reasons why a fraction is a bugbear. The first reason is that one single bear wears so many disguises. For example take Mr. Bear who generally signs his name: "One-half." For short, his old-fashioned initials were: $\frac{1}{2}$. Sometimes, especially when his initials appear in print, you see it printed: 1–2 or 1/2. Or it may take the form of $\frac{2}{4}$ or $\frac{4}{8}$ or $\frac{17}{34}$ or $\frac{50}{100}$. At the time of the French Revolution, this last form grew immensely in popularity. Instead of writing out the fraction, five-tenths, or fifty-hundredths, or five hundred-thousandths like this, $\frac{5}{10}$, $\frac{50}{100}$, $\frac{500}{1000}$, these French revolutionaries created no end of a stir by introducing a very tiny abbreviation.

Here is all it was: · Yes, that is absolutely all it was, a very simple little harmless dot. The blade of the guillotine had fallen on the neck of all the old-fashioned fractions. They now could be written like whole numbers, except that they had to stay behind the dot or decimal point. Furthermore, they could be treated in addition and subtraction, multiplication and division, just like whole numbers, providing the decimal point was properly managed. Our old friend, one-half, in his new French disguise became: 0.5 or 0.50 or 0.500.

However, it makes no difference what coat the bugbear wears, he has to be treated for what he is, a fraction! He will confuse you if he can, and in the early stages of your acquaintance with him in nine cases out of ten, he does. The reason is that he looks you square in the eye and says, "I'm a complicated and confusing critter," instead of your looking *him* square in the eye and saying, "Oh, no you're *not!*"

Take our old friend, "One-half," for example. He meets you in the woods and says, "What is one-half times one-half?" (That is of course only one-half of $\frac{1}{2}$ and anyone knows that half of half an apple pie is a quarter of an apple pie.) So you reply, "One-quarter, to be sure."

Then Mr. One-Half Bugbear continues, "But is one-half divided by one-half, 1?" You rub your eyes a bit. The idea is somewhat confusing, making whole numbers out of fractions. Had he said, "Is one-half divided by one-quarter 2?" it might at first be even more confusing.

The whole trouble arises from our not looking fractions square between the eyes and seeing what they are talking about.

For instance $\frac{1}{2} \times \frac{1}{2} = \frac{1}{4}$. Multiply the numerators, the numbers above the line, and multiply the denominators, the numbers below the line, which means, take half of one-half; and of course you get one-quarter.

But $\frac{1}{2} \div \frac{1}{2} = 1$. Invert the divisor and multiply. Leave the number to be divided alone but turn the dividing tool upside down and then proceed as in multiplying. The confusion comes because the real question is not clear. The real question is: "How many times does the dividing tool, $\frac{1}{2}$, go into the number to be divided?" Well, of course $\frac{1}{2}$ goes into $\frac{1}{2}$ exactly once, and $\frac{1}{4}$ goes into $\frac{1}{2}$ twice. Furthermore $\frac{1}{8}$ goes into $\frac{1}{2}$ four times and $\frac{1}{76}$ goes into $\frac{1}{2}$ thirty-eight times.

How does it work with the new-fangled French decimal fractions? Multiply 0.5 by 0.5. Remember that is just $\frac{1}{2} \times \frac{1}{2}$. The decimals might just as well have been written $\frac{5}{10} \times \frac{5}{10}$ and the answer would have been $\frac{25}{100}$. *That* is the answer when written in the shorthand of decimals: $0.5 \times 0.5 = 0.25$. In other words, treat the numbers behind the decimal point as though they were whole numbers; but point off as many places as there are in both the number to be multiplied and the multiplying tool.

In dividing, you subtract from the decimal places in the thing to be divided the number of places in the tool and point off the difference in the answer. For example: $0.5 \div 0.5 = 1$, or $0.500 \div 0.5 = 1.00$ which is the same thing.

As we take one parting look at arithmetic, "the science of numbers," it is just a little comforting to think over some of the difficulties we have missed. The Arabic figures which we use in adding and subtracting, in multiplying and dividing, are certainly a great deal better than the Roman X's, C's, I's, M's and V's. They make a much simpler multiplication table than one made with Greek *alphas, betas,* and *gammas.* We can be thankful for the decimal system which lets us work with our fractions as though they were whole numbers and count our money in dimes and dollars instead of having to say, "Four farthings, one penny; twelve pence, one shilling; twenty shillings, one pound."

As we look into the future, however, we should not think that the wonders of science, even in the old science of numbers, are at an end. We still measure our distances in inches, feet, yards, and miles — one inch $\times$ 12 equals one foot; one foot $\times$ 3 equals one yard; one yard $\times$ 1,760 equals one mile or 63,360 inches; while one centimeter $\times$ 100 equals one meter; and one meter $\times$ 1,000 equals one kilometer. This is a much simpler system than inches, feet, yards, and miles. The pound we use to weigh gold and silver is a 12-ounce pound. For meat and butter we use the equally clumsy 16-ounce pound. The troy pound is not $\frac{3}{4}$ of the avoirdupois pound as you would suspect, but about $\frac{4}{5}$ of it. Millions of people do their shopping and figure their prices much more easily and quickly by using grams and kilograms, that is 1,000 grams. New advantages of the science of numbers are ours for the asking. In fact, we don't need to ask for them. Just take them.

The Weighing Balances

ALGEBRA

ABOUT eight hundred years after the birth of Christ and two hundred years before Europeans started to rescue the Christian Holy Land from the Saracens, there lived an Arab mathematician named Mohammed ibn Mus Al-Khowarizmi. Like Euclid, whom we shall meet in geometry, he wrote a textbook. Unless we are guarded in our thinking we are inclined to confuse Euclid with the discoverers of geometry. Such of course is not the case. We know that geometry developed slowly through many hundreds of years. Euclid's books merely preserved for us the record of the discoveries. Al-Khowarizmi did not *invent* algebra. He was learned in the field of algebra but he acquired his learning from the many Arab mathematicians who preceded him. But he did call the process, "algebra."

The whole idea behind algebra is that as long as you start with two things that are equal, and then treat both of them the same, the results will be equal. Al-Khowarizmi might illustrate his principle by starting with one apple in each side of a weighing balance. After adding one apple to the right-hand side, he had to add one to the left-hand side. So long as he treated both pans equally, the scales remained in balance.

This may seem a very simple principle on which to develop a large and useful branch of mathematics, but that is all there is to it! The catch comes in being sure that you *always* treat *both* sides of the balance with absolute equality.

We have seen that with one apple in each side of the balance, if you add an apple to one side you must add another apple to the other side to keep the balance. (Of course it goes without saying that we are using apples of the same size.)

With two apples in each weighing pan, if we subtract one apple from one side we must take an apple away from the other side.

We may cut each apple in half, that is divide both sides by two, and our balance remains — our equation remains true or in balance. Or we may multiply each side by the same number and the balance remains. We may put ten times as many apples in one pan if we put ten times as many in the other.

Instead of considering apples only, suppose we use plums and apples. Two plums weigh just as much as one apple. We must have two plums in one pan if we have one apple in the other pan to start with. Then, if we add one apple to one side, we must add two plums to the other. If we cut the apple in half and take out one half, we would have to take out one plum. If we multiplied the number of apples by ten, we would have to multiply two plums by ten and have twenty plums in one pan to balance ten apples in the other pan.

If we call our apples "a" and our plums "b" — and this is what the Arabs did — this is the way the story could be put down in the shorthand of algebra:

$a = 2b$ (One apple equals two plums.)

$a + a = 2b + 2b$ (If you add one apple, you must add two plums to keep the balance equal.)

$\frac{a}{2} = b$ (If you cut one apple in half, you must cut the number of plums in half to keep the balance.)

$10a = 20b$ (So, ten times as many apples weigh as much as ten times as many pairs of plums.)

So much for the short system. Let's try to work out a troublesome problem in arithmetic but a very simple one in algebra.

John is ten years old. His father is 35 years old. After how many years will the father be twice as old as the son?

If all one knows is arithmetic, he must start by adding a few years to each age. Five years added to each makes the ages 15 and 40. Not right! Ten years added, 20 and 45. Still not right! Fifteen years added, 25 and 50. Right! But this "cut-and-try" method isn't satisfactory.

Let's do it by algebra. First we plan how we are going to use our weighing balance. By adding a certain number of years to John's age and multiplying his future age by two, you have the father's age after that certain number of years.

That certain unknown number of years is designated by x in algebra. Why? No good reason. It's just custom to use the letters x, y, z for "unknowns."

So . . . when you add x years to John's age of 10 years, you get John's future age, $10 + x$ years. Multiply that by two and that will equal his father's age after x years have come and gone.

Twice $(10 + x) = 35 + x$

$20 + 2x = 35 + x$

Subtract x from each side of the balance.

$20 + x = 35$

Subtract 20 years from each side.

$x = 15$

And x is that unknown number of years which we started out to find. The answer to our problem is 15 years.

How does it prove itself to be correct? In 15 years, John who now is 10 years old will be 25 years old. Twice 25 years is 50 years. That will be exactly the age of his father who is now 35 and in 15 years will be 50 years old.

The algebra part of the problem really isn't hard at all. Once you have the two balance pans evenly loaded, you just take out one x from each side and then take out 20 years from each side. Actually the only trick was one of using your head. You knew that John's father in the future was to be twice as old as John, so actually what you did was to put John and his imaginary twin brother into one side of the balance to offset John's father in the other.

John, aged 10, on the left is outbalanced by his 35-year-old

father. On the right, John's father, carrying the weight of 15 more years, just balances John and his imaginary twin brother, each of whom is 25 years old.

Let's look at another more practical problem. The corner druggist is having difficulty selling mixed nuts at 80¢ a pound. Another store down the street is offering a "special" at 69¢ a pound with a few peanuts mixed in. Peanuts sell for only 40¢ a pound. The question is: to ten pounds of the 80¢ nuts, how many pounds of 40¢ peanuts must be added to make the selling price of the mixture 69¢?

Well, of course, one way would be to start off by adding a pound of peanuts to ten pounds of mixed nuts and dividing $8.40 by 11; by adding 2 pounds of peanuts and dividing $8.80 by 12, and so on. But it is difficult to take out peanuts from the mixture once you've put in too many! Algebra is so much more accurate!

The first thing you must decide on is what your unknown quantity will stand for. For example, in this case, you might let x be either the weight of the peanuts to be added or the weight of the total mixture. Let's have x equal the weight of the total mixture because then we can fill up one side of our algebraic balance pan with x pounds of mixed nuts (including peanuts) @ 69¢ a pound or $69x$ cents as the total selling price.

Obviously into the other side of the balance, we put the 10 pounds of 80¢ nuts. Now for the peanuts! The difference between the total weight of the new mixture and 10 pounds is accounted for by peanuts, or $x - 10$ pounds of peanuts. And they cost only 40¢ a pound, or $40(x - 10)$ cents.

So 800¢ plus ($x - 10$ pounds) times 40¢ equals 69¢ times x pounds.

Or $800 + 40(x - 10) = 69x$

Or $800 + 40x - 400 = 69x$. (Take $40x$ out of both sides.)

$400 = 29x$

$x = 13.79$ pounds.

So we keep on adding peanuts until the total mixture weighs 13.79 pounds. Or we add 3.79 pounds of peanuts to the ten pounds of mixed nuts and sell them for 69¢ a pound and everyone is happy.

Does the druggist come out all right on the new deal? Yes he does, right to the odd penny. Multiply 13.79 (pounds) by 69¢.

\$9.5151 is what he'll get when he sells the new mixture. Peanuts — 3.79 (pounds) at 40¢ or \$1.52. Add to this \$8.00 for ten pounds of 80¢ mixed nuts, making \$9.52. That's as close an answer as anyone could want. Of course it remains to be seen whether he actually sold the nuts at all; but that's a commercial problem and not one for algebra. Algebra is only a useful tool, not a guarantee of success in life.

Now that we begin to see how algebra works, let's just suppose for a moment that we wanted a price of 71¢ or 59¢ or 63¢ or any other reasonable price for that matter. All we would have to do would be to use that price in place of the 69¢ we chose, and we would soon have the required answer. Using algebra is really just like setting up a special machine and getting the required result. One important thing is, however, that you must know what you're doing. You must know how to drive the special machine. But then you'd better walk if you don't know how to ride a bicycle. You certainly had better walk if you don't know how to drive an automobile. But to learn how to ride a bicycle, how to drive an automobile, and how to work algebra are all very useful accomplishments. You get where you want to go so much sooner and with much more certainty. Without any one of the three, there are many places you can't get to at all.

Well, one place you can go with algebra is into the realm of "the great unknown." When someone says to you that a piece of wire is one inch long, you know what he means. When he tells you that a piece of tin is 1 foot by 2 feet, the meaning of that is clear. When he tells you that a portable radio is $13'' \times 9'' \times 5''$, you know that it isn't a midget and that it isn't too bulky either. But if someone were to tell you that something is $3 \times 5 \times 8 \times 17 \ldots$ then what?

The fourth dimension! Many public institutions and private sanitariums are filled with people who worried over *that one!* Algebra lets you use the fourth dimension. Of course you don't understand it. Neither do people understand electricity but they use it just the same. Furthermore, algebra lets you use the fifth or sixth or tenth dimension or any other dimension that you want to, and it comes in mighty handy. If men and women didn't know how to use high powers of numbers like that, there wouldn't be any Boulder Dams, or radar, or radio, or television, or atomic bombs or many other wonderful things.

Back in arithmetic we met a plain old friend, the number 22. You remember what it looked like in the cube. Let's look at it closely to see what it looks like: first in a straight line, then as the side of a square, and finally as the side of a cube.

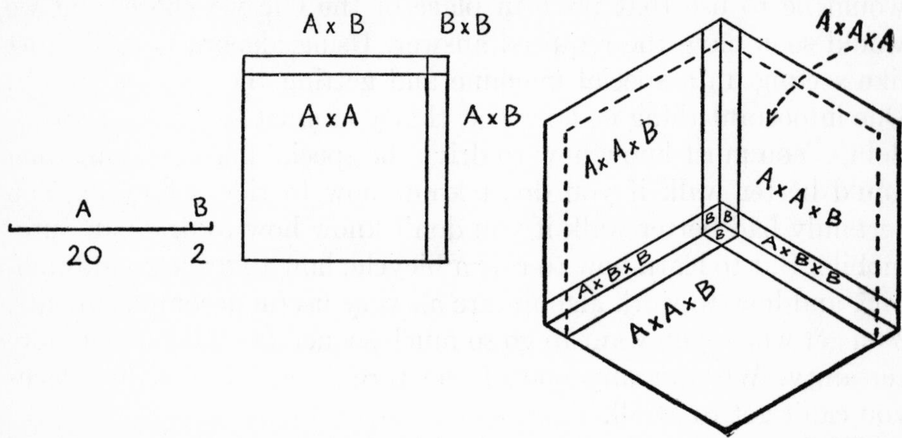

Our old friend "one score and two" or just plain 22 is simple enough to recognize in a straight line, although we don't frequently think of it as made up of two numbers. Abraham Lincoln thought of his numbers as made up of two separate numbers: "Fourscore and seven years ago, our forefathers . . ."

In a straight line, 22 is so familiar that we hardly ever think of it as made up of two numbers, two and twenty. In a square, we practically never think of it as 20×20 and 20×2 and 20×2 and 2×2 although that is precisely what 22×22 or 484 is. (Thinking back to square root in arithmetic, do you see how this sheds light on taking the square out of the hundreds first and then taking care of the remainder?)

In a cube, 22 gives us first a large cube $20 \times 20 \times 20$. Then it gives us three slabs $20 \times 20 \times 2$. Then it gives us three sticks $20 \times 2 \times 2$. Finally it gives us a tiny cube $2 \times 2 \times 2$.

Algebra merely puts in shorthand those stories so that they can be used to fit any two numbers that you want to square or cube.

$$(A + B)(A + B) \quad \text{or} \quad (A + B)^2 = A^2 + 2AB + B^2$$
$$(A + B)(A + B)(A + B) \quad \text{or} \quad (A + B)^3 = A^3 + 3A^2B + 3AB^2 + B^3$$

It's like the "boy meets girl" plot that you see over and over and over again in the movies. You know that the two of them are going to meet somewhere, somehow, sometime. (Otherwise there wouldn't be any movie.) Then they are going to fall in love and have all sorts of trouble. Then in the end . . . "and so they lived happily ever after."

The routine in the algebra "square plot" is as follows: you square the first, you multiply the first by the second twice, you square the second.

The "cube plot" in algebra is: cube the first, three times the first squared multiplied by the second (three slabs), three times the first multiplied by the square of the second (three sticks), and finally the second cubed (the little pip!).

Now don't fall off your chair. We actually have been doing some fairly complicated algebraic multiplication in our heads. Shocked, aren't you? You see it's really nothing at all when you aren't scared first by being told, "Next week we shall start in on the difficult subject of algebraic multiplication."

Having calmed down a bit after the shock, let us now make some rules. First we put the things to be multiplied down on paper just as

Squaring
$$\begin{array}{r} A + B \\ A + B \\ \hline A^2 + AB \qquad \\ AB + B^2 \\ \hline A^2 + 2AB + B^2 \end{array}$$

Cubing
$$\begin{array}{r} A^2 + 2AB + B^2 \qquad \\ A + B \qquad\qquad \\ \hline A^3 + 2A^2B + AB^2 \qquad \\ A^2B + 2AB^2 + B^3 \\ \hline A^3 + 3A^2B + 3AB^2 + B^3 \end{array}$$

we do in arithmetic. Then we multiply by A, then by B, and then add them up. To get the cube, we repeat the operation on the square.

All right. Hold your nose. Shut your eyes. Jump! We are about to plunge down and down and down into the unknown. The fourth, fifth, sixth, or seventh dimension. No one has ever been there except in his imagination. Of course if you dive off a ten-foot springboard with your eyes open, keep them open now too.

Let's just multiply that cube of (A + B) just once more by (A + B).

Raising to the Fourth Power

$$\begin{array}{lllll} A^3 & + 3A^2B & + 3AB^2 & + B^3 & \\ A & + B & & & \\ \hline A^4 & + 3A^3B & + 3A^2B^2 & + AB^3 & \\ & A^3B & + 3A^2B^2 & + 3AB^3 & + B^4 \\ \hline A^4 & + 4A^3B & + 6A^2B^2 & + 4AB^3 & + B^4 \end{array}$$

Do you see the plot? A few more complications before the end to be sure, but the plot follows a standard pattern. At the beginning is A^4, at the end is B^4. In between are AB, AB, and AB. Starting out alone, A, which has been multiplied by itself four times over, becomes A^4 and then promptly proceeds to run down like a clock, A^3, A^2, and finally just A^1. On the other hand, B is absent at the start, catches her breath slowly, and finishes strong: B^1, B^2, B^3, and finally B^4.

It is important to notice one other thing. Of course when A or B stands by itself, "one A" or "one B" is what is meant.

If we start to write down the arithmetic skeleton that creeps through the plot, here are the tracks left by that actor:

In squaring: 1 2 1

In cubing: 1 3 3 1

In raising to the Fourth Dimension: 1 4 6 4 1

Do you see how the arithmetic skeleton weaves his way through the lives of A and B? Can you guess who it was who is credited with the answer to the question of how that part of the plot spins out and out and out? None other than the poet, Omar Khayyám. You know his famous lines about resting in the shade of a tree with "a Book of Verses . . . and Thou."

That's just how far he was when we leaned over his shoulder, back there in A.D. 1100 or thereabouts. Why that is just a few years after the blond Franco-Norwegian, William, had pushed his Viking ships off the beaches in Normandy, down the Seine, and across the English Channel to make "Hasty Pudding" out of the Saxons at Hastings. Oxford town was just a wide spot in the road where a few poor starving students lived because they could listen to an odd lecture now and then. America? You wouldn't need to "give it back to the Indians." They had it already, or rather . . . still.

But in Bagdad . . . (You know — Abrabian Nights — Shieks — Splendor — White steeds!) the wise men had picked up, in A.D. 470, where the Greeks had left off. They pushed ahead in arithmetic, using plus and minus signs and the superior Arab numbers. When the sixth century rolled around (you always want to be careful to remember that the "sixth century" means the 500's) the Arabs in Bagdad were doing fractions much as we do them now. They also had discovered the use of "zero," without which we couldn't use our arithmetic the way we do.

In the year 800 a university with a very good department in mathematics was started in Bagdad. Here we meet our old friend, Professor Mohammed ibn Mus Al-Khowarizmi, or Alkarismi for short. And three hundred years later comes Omar Khayyám, with whom we are sitting under a fig tree.

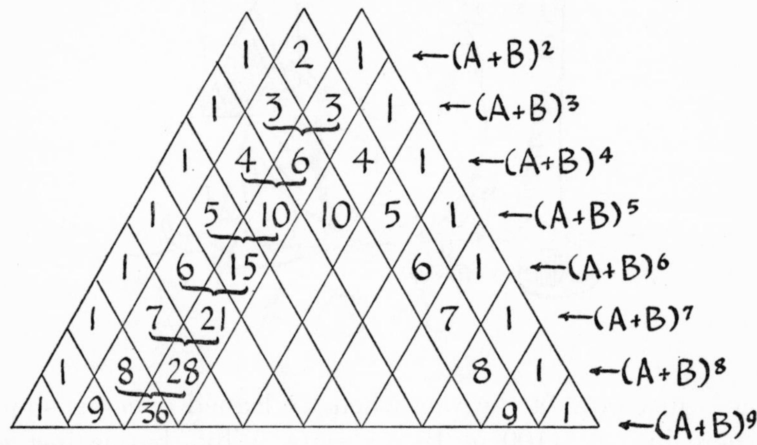

In the picture you notice that the first diagonal column and the last are filled with 1's . . . 1, 1, 1, 1, 1, 1.

The next inside columns both on the left and right are: 2, 3, 4, 5, 6, 7 and so on.

But do you see how he had filled the third columns? He added 3 and 3 together and put in 6. (Well, we knew that already because we had multiplied $(A + B)^4$.) Then he added the 4 and the 6 and put down 10; the 5 and the 10 and put down 15; the 15 and the 6 and put down 21 and so on down through the third diagonal columns.

What about the fourth diagonal columns? Add 10 and 10 and put down 20. Add 15 and 20 and put down 35. You see how the pyramid of numbers works in series.

When completed it looks like this:

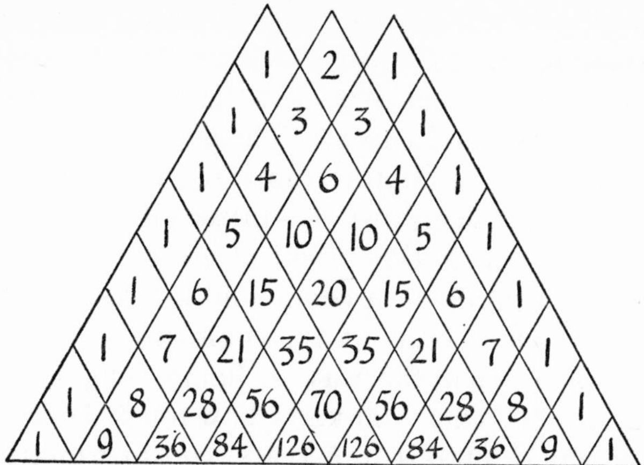

Now suppose we want to write down straight off $(A + B)^9$. It's quite a lot of work to multiply $(A + B)$ over and over again nine times. All we really need to do is let A run down, let B wind up, and put in the arithmetic skeleton numbers:

$$A^9 \quad A^8 \quad A^7 \quad A^6 \quad A^5 \quad A^4 \quad A^3 \quad A^2 \quad A$$

$$B \quad B^2 \quad B^3 \quad B^4 \quad B^5 \quad B^6 \quad B^7 \quad B^8 \quad B^9$$

$$9 \quad 36 \quad 84 \quad 126 \quad 126 \quad 84 \quad 36 \quad 9$$

$$A^9 + 9A^8B + 36A^7B^2 + 84A^6B^3 + 126A^5B^4 + 126A^4B^5 + 84A^3B^6 + 36A^2B^7 + 9AB^8 + B^9$$

Simple little triangle, isn't it when you once see it! Well, Omar, the poet, worked it out back there under the tree, or maybe it was taught in the University of Bagdad and Omar gets the credit for it. Anyway, it was not until several hundred years later that scholars in Western Europe had it passed on to them through traders with the East who lived in Italy.

If, after all this, you feel quite strong, perhaps it will be safe to tell you that you have just been exposed to a very severe case of the binomial theorem. Of course, in real life, you probably will never be exposed to the ninth dimension; but it has not been too bitter a pill. Probably the worst you will encounter are the fourth or fifth dimension, and you can toss those off like nothing at all.

But perhaps you are asking, "Is there anything real in that world beyond squares and cubes?" The answer is yes, indeed!

How do you like to compute compound interest? Well, neither does anyone else. However, just as a bitter pill which we shall take for having asked about the practical benefits of the binomial theorem, let's do a problem in compound interest. How much will $172.50 amount to in 5 years at 4% compound interest?

Everyone knows that the way to figure compound interest is to figure it on $1.00. When you know how much $1.00 will amount to at 4% compound interest in 5 years, you just multiply that by $172.50 and you save yourself a lot of work.

```
                                $1.00
                                 1.04
                                -----
                                .0400
                               1.00
                               ------
After 1 year                   1.04
                               1.04
                               ------
                                  416
                                1040
                               ------
After 2 years ($1.04)^2        1.0816
                                 1.04
                               ------
                                43264
                              108160
                              -------
After 3 years ($1.04)^3      1.124864
                                 1.04
                             --------
                              4499456
                            11248640
                            ---------
After 4 years ($1.04)^4    1.16985856
                                 1.04
                           ----------
                            467943424
                          1169858560
                          -----------
After 5 — ($1.04)^5      1.2166529024
```

After one year, the dollar has earned 4¢ interest and has become $1.04. The $1.04 has earned $.04\frac{16}{100}$¢ at the end of the second year. For simplicity, just multiply $1.04 by $1.04. In other words, square \$1.04 to get the total at the end of two years. The $(\$1.04)^3$ is the total at the end of three years; $(\$1.04)^4$ at the end of four years; and $(\$1.04)^5$ is the total of principal and compound interest at the end of five years.

But what a lot of work it has been to find out the hard way that \$1.00 grows to \$1.2167 at the end of five years!

It doesn't take much imagination to call \$1.04, "\$1.00 plus .04." In other words A is \$1 and B is \$0.04. To raise (A + B) to the fifth power, that is multiply it by itself five times over as we did above, all we have to do is to let A run down and wind up B and put on the pyramid numbers starting with 1 . . . 5 . . . 10 . . . etc. So $(A + B)^5$ is

"A" running down	A^5	A^4	A^3	A^2	A	
"B" winding up		B	B^2	B^3	B^4	B^5
The pyramid numbers, 1, 5, 10, etc......	1	5	10	10	5	1

$$A^5 + 5A^4B + 10A^3B^2 + 10A^2B^3 + 5AB^4 + B^5$$

Now instead of all that arithmetic, which results in ten figures behind the decimal point most of which are useless, we use $(A + B)^5$:

A^5	which is	1 x 1 x 1 x 1 x 1	1.00
$5A^4B$	which is	5 x 1 x 1 x 1 x 1 x .04	.20
$10A^3B^2$	which is	10 x 1 x 1 x 1 x .04 x .04	.016

(Do you see that our new answer is already correct to 3 decimal places)?

$10A^2B^3$	which is	10 x 1 x 1 x .04 x .04 x .04	.00064

(It's correct now to 4 places, but let's go on to the bitter end).

$5AB^4$	which is	5 x 1 x .04 x .04 x .04 x .04	.0000128
B^5	which is	.04 x .04 x .04 x .04 x .04	.0000001024
Adding up....			\$1.2166529024

Have you a penny? That's to make change for a quarter. Because, if you had \$100,000,000, at the end of five years at 4% compound interest it would amount to \$121,665,290 and 24¢.

But really Omar probably never worried much about that 1¢ change as he sat there in the shade with his back against the tree.

The fifth dimension! You can't draw a picture of it but you can draw interest with it.

P.S. Oh yes, about the \$172.50 @ 4% compound interest for five years, we still have to multiply it by the amount to which \$1.00 will grow in five years, that is \$1.2167 × \$172.50 and the answer is \$209.88.

Egyptian Rope-Swingers

GEOMETRY

IF you had been sailing down the Nile River in Egypt about the year 1700 B.C., you might have thought that the two men you saw on the shore were getting ready to officiate at a football game. There they were swinging a rope along the flat rich field on the

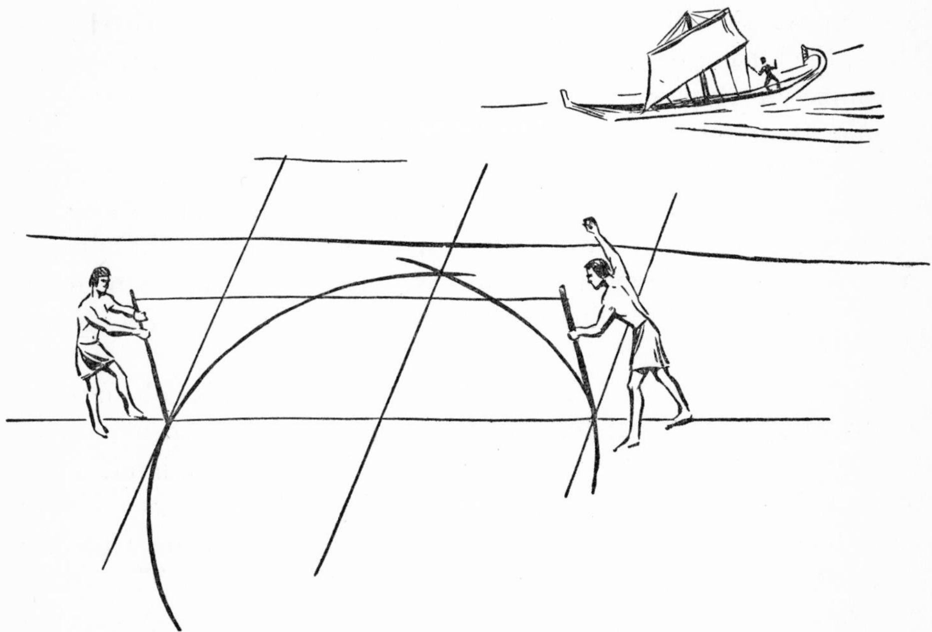

river bank. The rope was attached to two poles and looked exactly the same as the set of poles and ropes used to measure first downs at a modern football game.

You would have been wasting your time to go ashore and wait for the game . . . in 1700 B.C. The "linesmen" were getting ready for spring planting. Father Nile had just receded after flooding the fields with rich alluvial soil. The annual flooding process made the narrow ribbon of land through the sandy desert the garden spot of north Africa and the home of an ancient civilization. That is, the Nile made it possible for the Egyptians to eat. But first, they had to use their heads.

Well, these rope-swingers actually were gentlemen and scholars practicing applied geometry. Only the Egyptians didn't call it geometry. It wasn't until more than a thousand years later that "geo" measuring got going under it's Greek title. (Geo means "the earth" and from it we get words like earth-writing or earth-drawing, geography, as well as earth-measuring, geometry.) To the Egyptians, the business was just plain rope-swinging. Certainly, passing a course in Rope-swinging I or Rope-swinging II would seem simpler than passing Geometry I or Geometry II.

Well, what were the rope-swingers doing? They were measuring off rectangular fields of equal sizes for the farmers and slaves to cultivate. They started with a long line between two stakes on the river front. When they had measured off say ten lengths of rope, they decided to run a line inland, making the corner of a square with the shore line.

Here's what they did. The fellow upstream held his pole in place and the fellow downstream swung his rope and pole and made two circular marks, one on the river bank and the other inland. Then he went back to his position and the other fellow did as the first had done. The two places where the marks crossed lined up the boundary of two fields running back from the river. Then they did the same thing again and again, and by nightfall they had the big field divided up into neat rectangular fields ready for planting.

It didn't take much of a brain to be a rope-swinger in the early Egyptian school of geometry. The game wasn't learned out of books. It was just a part of the everyday business of life. After you

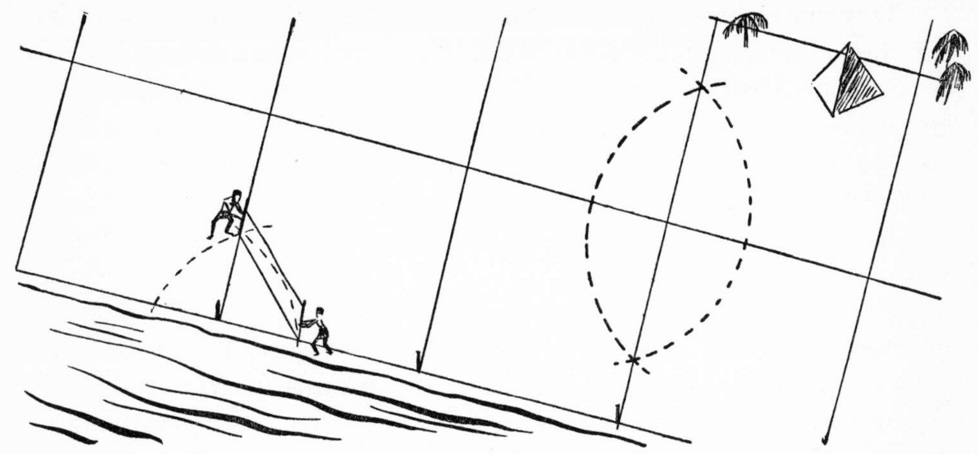

had learned how to divide up a field into squares, the problem might arise quite naturally, how divide an angle into two equal angles?

First one rope-swinger would go to the point where the two sides of the angle met. The other rope-swinger would scratch marks across the sides of the angle. Then one would scratch a line while the other held his pole where the first scratch crossed the side of the angle. Then the second fellow would do the same thing from the other side of the angle. Where the second and third scratches crossed was a new point which divided the angle into two equal parts. This was practical, every-day rope-swinging in Egypt in the year 1700 B.C. There's nothing difficult about it. However, by the time this very simple operation found its way into Greek geometry books more than 2,000 years later, complications arose.

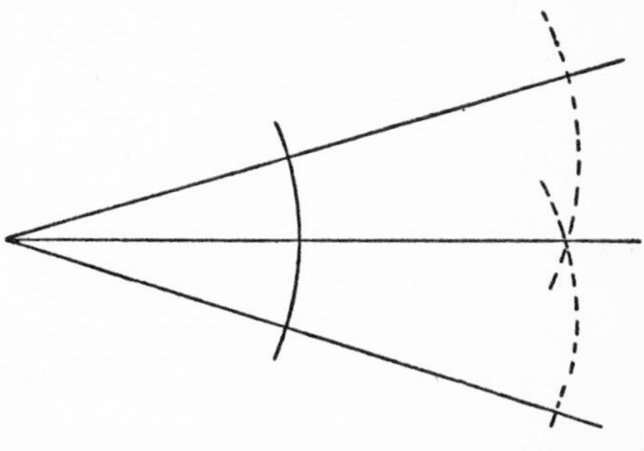

The Greeks made this simple job, bisecting an angle, into an exercise in mental gymnastics. You had to *prove* that the two angles were equal.

By the time the simple Egyptian rope-swinging job appeared in English books about geometry 3,000 years later, it had acquired a famous name. Of course any dunce could divide an angle equally into two angles. That was not the point. You had to prove it. If you could talk about it logically and prove that you had divided the angle into two equal angles, you were allowed to go across the *Pons Asinorum*, "Jackass Bridge," and study some more geometry. Either you got across the bridge or you didn't. Those who didn't were jackasses!

Quite a long distance on the other side of *Pons Asinorum* is a famous triangle. It was known to the Egyptians in 1700 B.C. It is called the magic "3-4-5 triangle." The Egyptians probably didn't discover its magic. Quite likely they learned about it from the Babylonians, who lived far across the Red Sea and the Arabian Desert in the valleys of the Tigris and Euphrates Rivers. At least tablets made out of baked clay and dated about 2,000 B.C. show that the Babylonians knew about the famous 3-4-5 triangle. We are going to see a great deal more of this famous triangle during the next 4,000 years; so it will be interesting to look at it as it was known to the Babylonians in 2,000 B.C. Both the Babylonians and the Egyptian rope-swingers started with a line on which they measured off 4 lengths with their poles. Then they made the corner of a square and measured off 3 lengths on that line. When they connected the far end of the 3 line to the far end of the 4 line and measured the distance, what do you think they found?

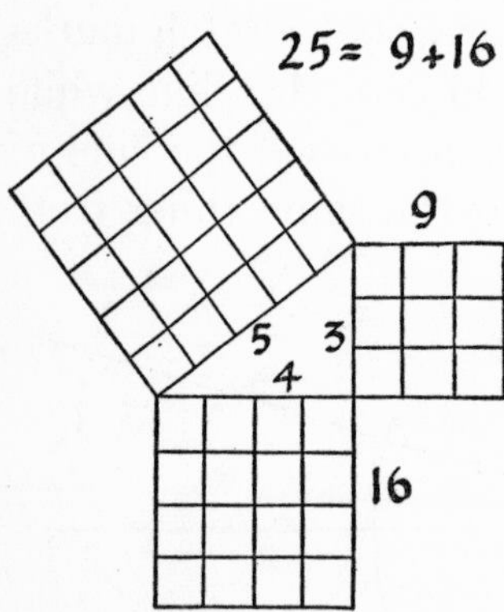

By Jimminy (or something stronger to that effect) it measured *exactly* 5 lengths!

Over and over again they measured it to make sure, and it always came out 5 lengths. Now this is the strange thing about it:

make a square on the 3 side, on the 4 side, and on the 5 side. The square on the 3 side has 9 squares in it. The square on the 4 side has 16 squares in it. Add them together, $9 + 16 = 25$, which is exactly the number of squares in the large square on the 5 side. So here was a magic triangle in which the square on the largest side equalled the squares on the 2 smaller sides added together.

That's as much as the Babylonians and the Egyptians learned or took the trouble to learn about it for 1,500 years. That thought should console one if he or she is a bit slow in picking up geometry. The human race took about 1,500 years to make the next important step with that famous triangle. So don't reach up to feel for long ears sticking through the brim of your hat if you're still on this side of Jackass Bridge. It isn't entirely fair to expect you to pick up in fifteen minutes of homework some night after school, something which took the human race 1,500 years to find out!

Mr. Pythagoras was a Greek who was in his prime about 550 B.C. He lived much of his life in the Greek colony on the lower tip of Italy. He was deeply interested in this business of "earth measuring." In other words he was a "geometer." But he wasn't satisfied with the pleasant, useful ways of the Egyptians. The gentlemen in Greece were bitten by a thing called the "scientific spirit." Times were prosperous. The slaves did most of the muscle work. Fine marble temples were being built. Gentlemen met in the market place and after discussing city politics, branched out into other subjects such as — well, geometry.

You have seen pictures of the marble-paved market places of ancient Greece. Well, according to legend (and for our purposes one yarn is just about as good as another) Mr. Pythagoras sat there one day staring at the marble pavement.

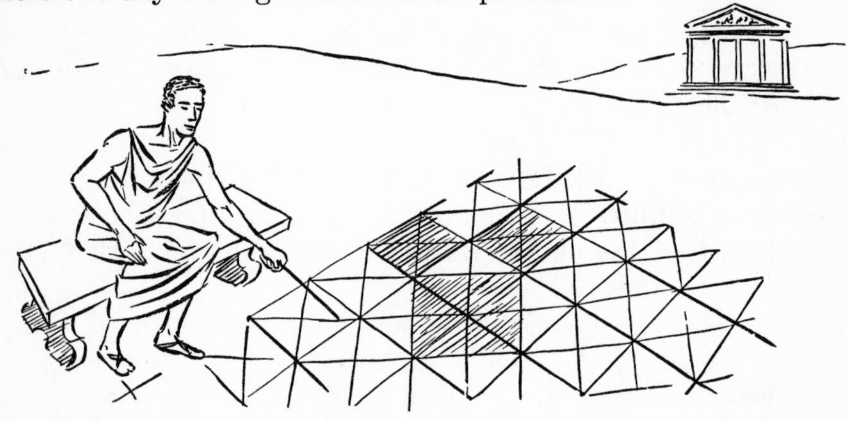

He knew that the marble cutters always had considerable difficulty in keeping the large square marble paving slabs from cracking across the middle. So the architect had given them a smaller triangular pattern which represented just half a square. That made the marble cutters' work easier. Besides, it made the design somewhat more attractive when the slabs were put in place in the pavement.

Pythagoras found it not only more attractive but exceedingly interesting.

"There you have another triangle with the corner of a square in it," he said pointing to a group of paving slabs. "Now the square on the side that holds up that triangle has four paving slabs in it. The squares on the two other sides of the triangle each have two paving slabs in them. Four slabs equal four slabs.

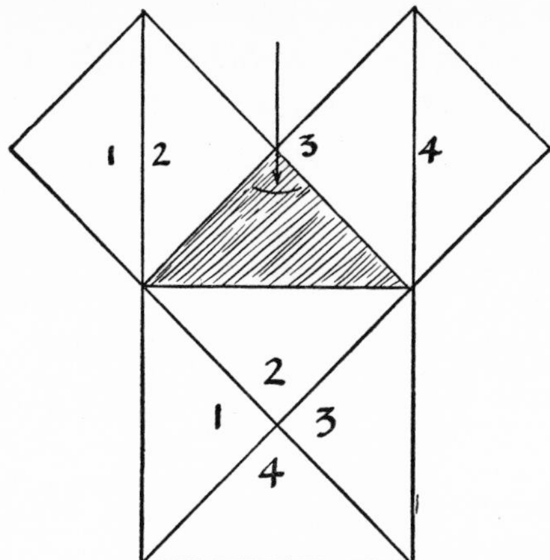

"So here, gentlemen, we have another triangle containing the corner of a square. As in the historic Babylonian, or perhaps one should say Egyptian, 3-4-5 triangle, the square constructed on the sustaining side is the same size as the squares constructed on the two other sides when you add them together!"

Frankly, Pythagoras must have been quite pleased with himself. The Greek scientific spirit was at work. Observation. To be scientific, the first thing necessary is to have a very keen eye.

"Very true. Very true indeed . . . but . . ." said one of the group. There, it was coming! Someone said "but." It seems that even in Greek times there had to be at least *one* at every party.

"But," said the doubting Thomas, clearing his throat, "with the Babylonian triangle the two sides other than the hypotenuse . . ." (He was using the four-dollar Greek word for the under (hypo) side.) "As I was saying, the square of the hypotenuse in the 3-4-5 triangle equals the sum of the squares of the other sides only under *very* special conditions. One of the sides must be exactly three and the other exactly four units long.

"Now, Pythagoras, in your new example today," Thomas continued, "you, too, impose another very special condition. You insist that the two smaller sides be equal. But supposing I make any right triangle, let's see how your marble cutters can help you out in proving that one!" And he drew an odd-shaped right triangle in the dust covering the marble pavement.

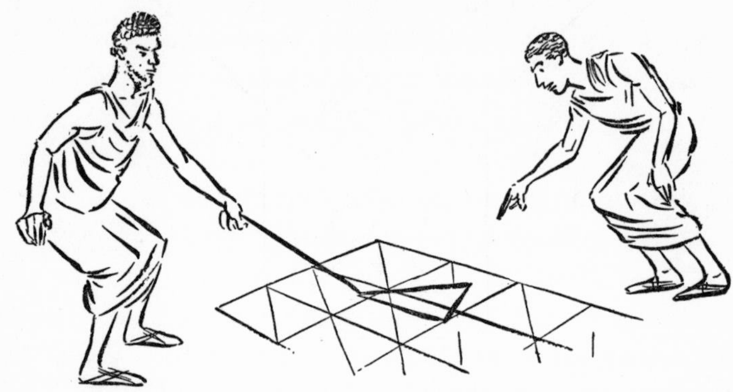

That broke up the meeting for the day. Pythagoras hadn't particularly liked the manner of doubting Thomas; but still he had to admit that the man showed the true Greek scientific spirit. Two specially selected cases, such as the 3-4-5 triangle and the paving block triangle, don't prove anything. You must select your samples *at random.* You must be able to prove a scientific truth about right triangles *in general* by using *any* right triangle.

Nevertheless, Pythagoras was convinced that he was on the right track. For a long time he turned over in his mind both the 3-4-5 triangle and the paving block triangle. Thinking to himself, he used a kind of shorthand. He gave the sides of the triangles short names: *alpha* or a for one of the two shorter sides, *beta* or b for the other short side, and h for the *hypotenuse.* In Greek hypotenuse means a thing which supports something, or holds it up from the under (*hypo*) side (*tenuse*). Since the hypotenuse was opposite the largest of the three angles in the triangle, that is the corner of a square or a right angle, it was always the longest of the triangle's three sides.

Pythagoras reasoned this way to himself. In the 3-4-5 triangle, a being 3 and b being 4, their squares were 9 and 16 which added up to 25 and, as that was the same as hypotenuse squared, he wrote it down as h^2.

In the paving block triangle, there were 2 paving blocks in the square on the *a* side, 2 paving blocks in the square on the *b* side, and 4 paving blocks in the square on the *h* side.

But in doubting Thomas' triangle whose *a* and *b* sides were of *any* length whatsoever, Pythagoras was at a complete loss for the time being.

Then Pythagoras made another triangle for himself. Side *a* was still 3, but side *b* was so small you could hardly see it. The square on *h* was almost identical with the square on *a*. In fact the naked eye could hardly detect the difference. Pythagoras suspected that h^2 was just a tiny bit larger than a^2 and that tiny bit he suspected was b^2. But he had to prove it!

Following the rules which guided those filled with the true Greek scientific spirit, the next thing which Pythagoras did was to set down in clear and orderly fashion the results of his observations. Here is a picture of what he had to consider. By looking at it

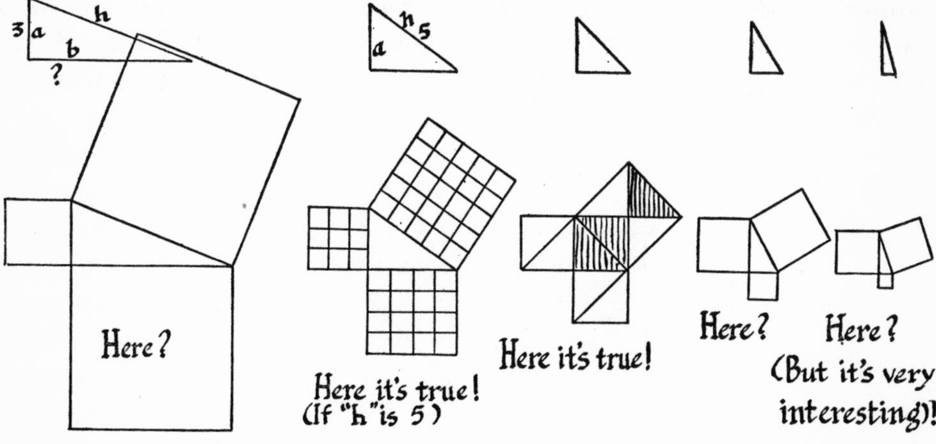

carefully, one can see why Pythagoras was certain that he was on the right track. One can imagine why he was annoyed, more perhaps with himself than with doubting Thomas, for not being able to prove that the square of *any* hypotenuse is equal to the sum of the squares of the other two sides.

It isn't often that you can sit and look at all the facts which a great discoverer had before him a few days or hours preceding the moment when the discovery was made. What was Mr. Bell thinking about the day he invented the telephone? What did Mr. Morse have on paper when he invented the telegraph? What was in the laboratory the night before Mr. Edison made his first electric light bulb? Well, you are looking at nearly all the facts and doubts which Pythagoras had before him when he made one of the greatest mathematical discoveries of all times! You might look at them for hours and days, and many other people might look at them for weeks and months and years, and nothing would happen. After all, hadn't Babylonians and Egyptians looked at the 3-4-5 triangle for 1,500 years without finding out what Pythagoras did?

I suspect that what Pythagoras did was to take a slightly broader view of the paving block triangle. He may have looked at two of the small triangles which made up a larger triangle. The square on the hypotenuse now was made up of 8 paving blocks and each square on the two other sides had 4 paving blocks. But an exceedingly interesting line appeared. It was the line which

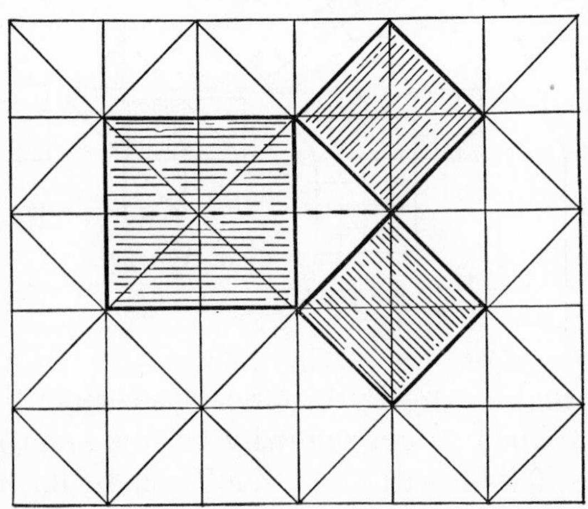

started at the corner of the right angle and was perpendicular to the hypotenuse. It ran across the square on the hypotenuse.

AND IT DIVIDED THE HYPOTENUSE SQUARE INTO EXACT HALVES! Each half had 4 paving blocks in it. Each of the smaller equal squares had 4 paving blocks in them. That perpendicular to the hypotenuse divided the hypotenuse square into very interesting parts!

Pythagoras was very excited. He rushed back to all the other triangles which he had drawn. He put in dotted lines from the right angle perpendicular to the hypotenuse. And this is what he saw.

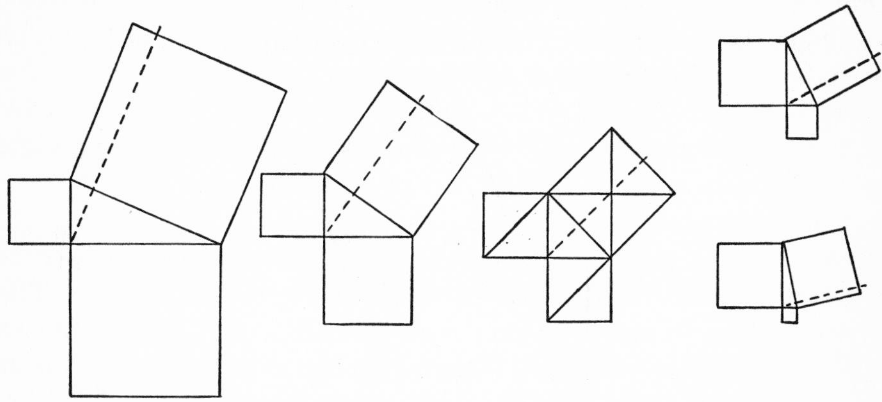

In the paving block triangle in which two of the sides were equal, the dotted line divided the hypotenuse square into exactly equal halves. In all the other triangles, the dotted line divided the hypotenuse square into two parts and the size of each part bore a striking resemblance to the size of the nearby square.

Pythagoras said to himself almost impatiently, "If I can only prove that!"

He had a fairly good supply of tools in the geometry workshop of the Greeks. After all, they had spent a great deal of time polishing up the crude tools of the Babylonians and the Egyptians and sharpening up some new tools of Greek design. He pulled out the tool which he needed. It was the tool to work with on the areas of figures with parallel sides.

It said that any figure with parallel sides, whether it was a square or a rectangle or a parallelogram, has an area equal to the product of its base and its altitude. And it said that a triangle had an area equal to one-half the product of its base and its altitude.

So Pythagoras started with any right triangle at all. Its sides, a and b could be any length at all. What he wanted to prove was that $a^2 + b^2 = h^2$.

After drawing the perpendicular to the hypotenuse from the right angle and extending it across the hypotenuse square, he had a rectangle. Half of its area was a triangle with the same base and altitude as the rectangle.

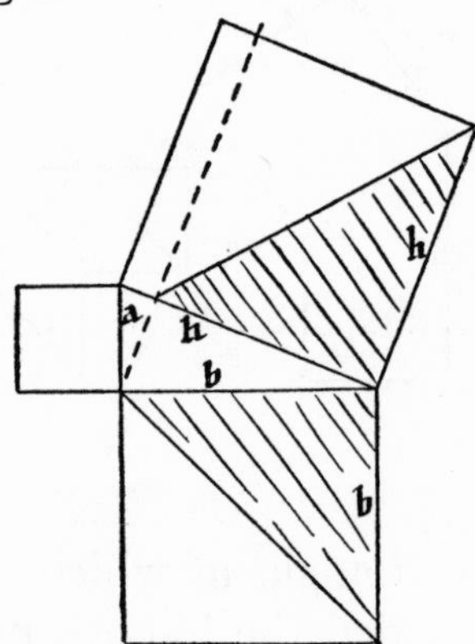

Half of the area of the lower square also was a triangle whose base was b and whose altitude also was b.

Now here comes the only tricky part of Pythagoras' work. He used the tool which told him that half of a parallelogram is the area of a triangle with the same base and altitude. He made the upper rectangle into a parallelogram and the lower square into another parallelogram. Then he cut both parallelograms in half.

Here were two most interesting triangles! Each triangle had h for one side and b for another side. The angle in each triangle where these two sides met was the same angle; because it was made up of a right angle plus the small angle opposite side a.

When two sides of a triangle and the angle between them are equal to two sides and the included angle of another triangle, *the two triangles are equal to each other.*

Pythagoras had his proof! Those two triangles which were equal to each other were halves of parallelograms. So-o the parallelograms

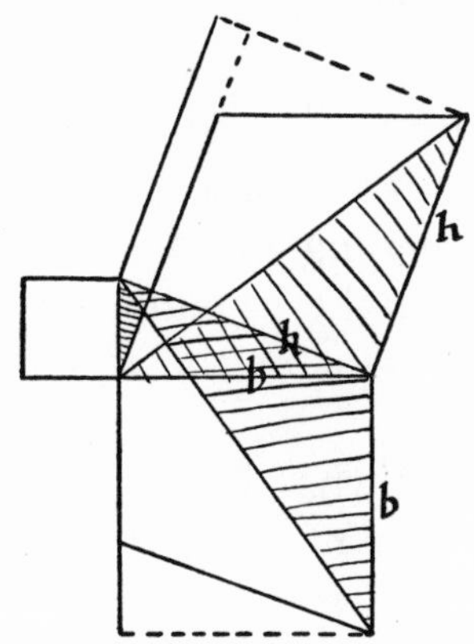

were equal; because when the halves are equal the wholes are equal. And the lower parallelogram was equal to the square on b and the upper parallelogram was equal to that part of h square cut off by the perpendicular to the hypotenuse.

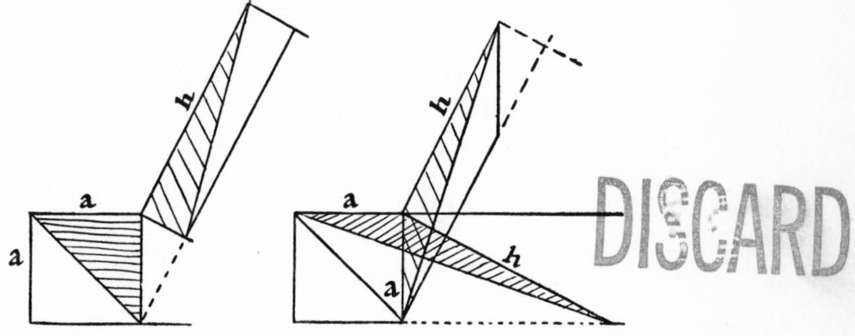

DISCARD

Now that Pythagoras had discovered the trick, he very quickly proved that the square on a was equal in area to the area of the long narrow strip cut off on its side of the perpendicular to the hypotenuse. The triangle with a for its base and a for its altitude was $\frac{1}{2}$ of a^2. It was equal to the triangle which had a for its base and h for one of its sides, because its altitude still was a.

The angle included between a and h was made up of a right angle and the corner of the original triangle opposite side b. Half of the long narrow parallelogram was a triangle which also contained this angle, the angle opposite b, and a right angle. The sides including this angle were a and h. With two sides and the included angle equal, the two triangles were equal. The parallelograms were equal. The rectangle and the square were equal.

When the two parts of the hypotenuse square were added together they equalled the sum of the squares on the sides in *any* right triangle whatsoever!

Pythagoras had proved what he set out to prove: *The square of the hypotenuse equals the sum of the squares of the other two sides.*

"Q.E.D." *Quod erat demonstrandum* — "Which was to be proved." (That is a quotation from Roman schoolmasters.)

Pythagoras went back to the meeting of his fellow Greek geometers the next day. He had his tongue in his cheek, waiting for doubting Thomas. Then he let Thomas have it from both barrels! Or rather from both squares, the left leg squared and the right leg squared with the square of the hypotenuse thrown in for good measure.

Of course in the days of the Greeks when Pythagoras lived, say 550 B.C., printing hadn't been invented. The minutes of the meetings of the geometers had to be very brief. They were all written and drawn by hand. So they resorted to a kind of shorthand. They used diagrams and letters. Here is the shorthand account of Pythagoras' discovery. It may be a little baffling, until you know what it is all about.

Theorem (that is a general proposition not self-evident but demonstrable by argument): In *any* right triangle, the square of the hypotenuse is equal to the sum of the squares of the legs.

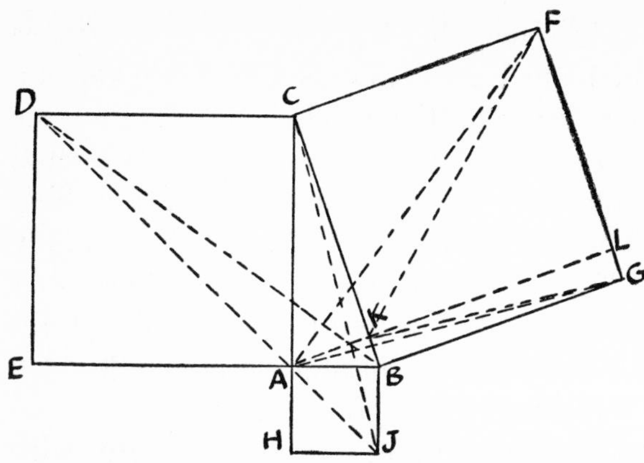

On *AB* at *A* erect the perpendicular *AC*.
Draw *BC* to form the right triangle *ABC*.
Construct the squares: *ACDE*, *ABJH*, *BCFG*.
From *A* erect the perpendicular to *BC*, extend it from *K* to *L*.
Draw: *KG*, *AG*; *JA*, *JC*; *DA*, *DB*; *FK*, *FA*.

Demonstration: The whole equals the sum of the parts. Therefore, *BCFG* equals *KCFL* plus *KLGB*. Therefore *ABJH* equals *ABJ* plus *AJH*; *ACDE* equals *ACD* plus *ADE*; *CFLK* equals *CFK* plus *FLK*, and *BGLK* equals *BGK* plus *KLG*.

Triangles with the same base and altitude are equal. Therefore *BJA* equals *BJC*; *BGK* equals *BGA*; *CFK* equals *CFA*; *CDA* equals *CDB*.

Triangles in which two sides and the included angle are equal are equal. Therefore *BJC* equals *ABG*; *CDB* equals *CFA*.

Conclusion: Therefore *BCFG* equals *ABJH* plus *ACDE*.

Quod erat demonstrandum. Q.E.D.

Proved? Clear . . . as mud. And no one could blame you for being a bit annoyed and saying so. You spend most of your time and energy chasing shorthand letters around the sides of squares and triangles. Maybe you try to memorize the complicated diagram and the more complicated and arbitrary system of lettering.

It is much more reasonable to be told how the whole question first arose. When one recalls that the Babylonians and the Egyptians knew about the magic 3-4-5 triangle for several hundred years and had to wait for help from very brainy Pythagoras, one feels better about the whole thing.

Well, about 200 years after Pythagoras another Greek named Euclid finally summarized almost everything the Greeks knew about geometry and put it in a neat textbook.

Euclid, who was a very logical gentleman, began his book in a very logical way. He began by definitions. Then he put in some axioms. An axiom is just a self-evident truth, such as "the sum of the parts equals the whole," or "things equal to the same thing are equal to each other." Then he inserted a chapter dealing mainly with the Babylonians and Egyptians and what they had picked up in a couple of thousand years about lines and angles and squares and triangles and cubes. Then came a chapter about circles and parts of circles and what happened when you put a triangle inside a circle or outside a circle. He went on and paired up squares with circles, five-sided figures, six-sided figures, and so on. That led to putting the finger on, not "in the pie." But that's a rather long story and we'll come to it later. Euclid went on next to cubes and all sorts of other solid figures. In other words he branched out from "plane" into "solid" geometry. Chapters followed about cylinders, cones, spheres, and that just about wound up what the Greeks knew about geometry.

After looking through Euclid's "Table of Contents," let's have a look at the plot. Let's start with the definitions. Now the Babylonians and the Egyptian rope-swingers hadn't bothered much about what a point was. That was where a rope-swinger held his pole while his partner indulged in "swing." But the Greeks, being scientific in spirit, had to define a "point."

"A point is that which has *no* dimension." That's a sort of negative way of saying something, but the reason for saying it that way will be apparent when you get on to the definition of a line. "A line is that which has *one* dimension." In other words, a line is that which has length only. It is the path left by a moving point. And what happens when you move or "generate" a line? You have a plane. It has *two* dimensions: the length of the line and the width of the plane. And what happens when you move or "generate" a plane? You have a solid, or that which has *three* dimensions: length, width, and thickness.

And what happens when you *move* or *generate* a *solid?* That's where you get into the fourth dimension and that has landed many a good man before you in a straight-jacket; so for the present, you'd do just as well to skip it. In algebra you can play not only with the fourth dimension, but also with the fifth and sixth and as many dimensions as you like, and none of them will be loaded or go off in your face and blow your brains out.

After Euclid's chapter on definitions, he takes up lines. There are two kinds of lines: straight lines and curved lines. A straight line is movement in one direction; a curved line is movement in more than one direction. In other words, if you start off to generate a point in one direction and only one direction, you generate a straight line; but if you indulge in two or more directions you generate a broken line or a curved line.

Euclid now starts to complicate the plot. He says, "What happens when you start with two points as your characters and introduce a straight line?" Between two points a straight line and but one can be drawn. Why? Well, from one point to another there is only one direction and therefore only one line.

Euclid goes to considerable pains to prove that if two straight lines meet, they meet at only one point. Although he lets you take for granted that the angles on one side of a line form a *straight* angle, or two right angles, he makes quite a fuss in proving that opposite angles made by intersecting straight lines are equal (Fig. 1).

Then he discusses triangles, when they are *congruent* and when they are not — that means, when one can be placed on top of another exactly. It's much simpler to say "triangles are equal." Well, triangles are equal when:

1 — Two sides and the included angle are equal (Fig. 2). (Pythagoras used that one!)
2 — Two angles and the included side are equal (Fig. 3).
3 — The three sides are equal (Fig. 4).

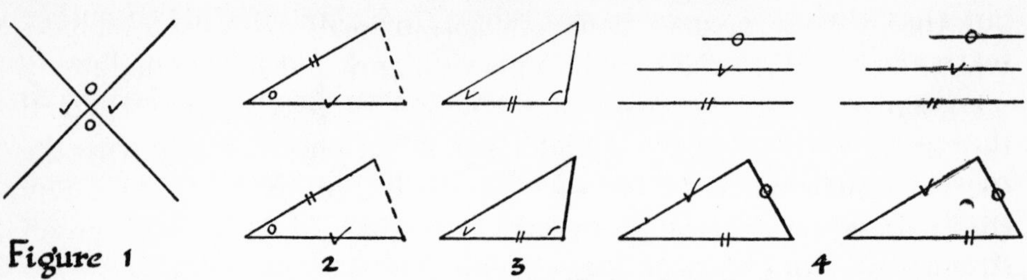
Figure 1 2 3 4

Euclid devotes a chapter to the Egyptian rope-swingers and their perpendiculars. How pompous he sounds: "At a point a perpendicular and but one can be drawn to a line" (Fig. 5); from a point . . . ditto . . . (Fig. 6). And then this one: "A perpendicular is the shortest distance from a point to a line!" (Fig. 7).

Two perpendiculars to a straight line are parallel because they will not meet however far they are extended (Fig. 8). Then he says that opposite angles are equal when parallel lines are cut by a line (Fig. 9). This leads to the interesting conclusion that the sum of the angles of a triangle is two right angles (Fig. 10).

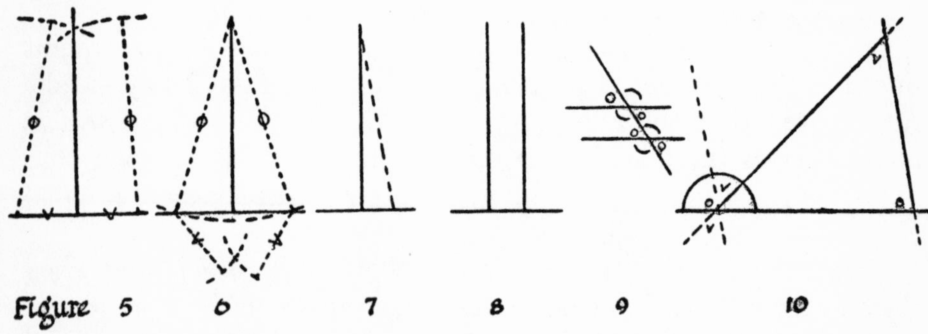
Figure 5 6 7 8 9 10

After many more details about triangles, Euclid puts in a chapter about the circle. Now what do you think a circle is? The Babylonians and the Egyptians and the Greeks had been drawing circles for centuries. In Euclid's book, a circle becomes the curved line, bounding part of a plane, all of whose points are equally distant from a point called the center. That's sort of defining the familiar but that's what a circle is, according to Euclid and all the other textbook writers ever since.

The circle has a radius: the straight line from the center to the circle itself (Fig. 1). It also has a diameter: a straight line twice the length of the radius (Fig. 2). Of course all radii in one circle are equal (Fig. 3). So are all diameters (Fig. 4). A part of a circle is an arc (Fig. 5). The straight line joining the ends of an arc is a chord (Fig. 5). Equal arcs measure equal angles at the center and equal central angles measure equal arcs (Fig. 6). A perpendicular to a radius at the circle is tangent to the circle (Fig. 7).

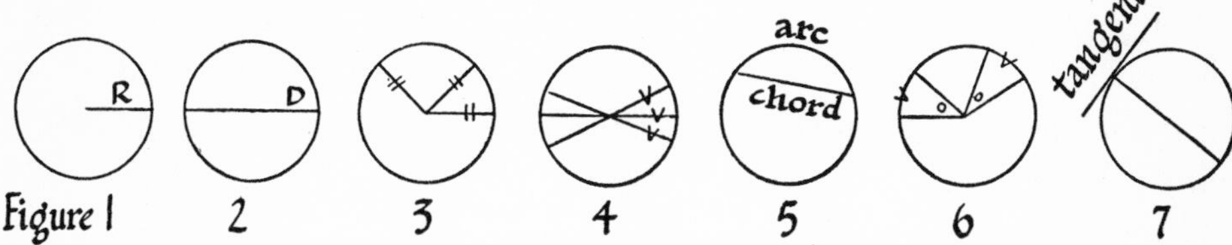

Figure 1 2 3 4 5 6 7

If two circles have a chord in common, the line connecting the centers cuts the chord in halves (Fig. 8). Angles go into circles in interesting ways. Every angle made by joining a point on the circle to the ends of a diameter is a right angle (Fig. 9). A circle can be drawn inside (Fig. 10) or outside any triangle (Fig. 11). But to do this you must have crossed the *Pons Asinorum!* You must know how to bisect an angle.

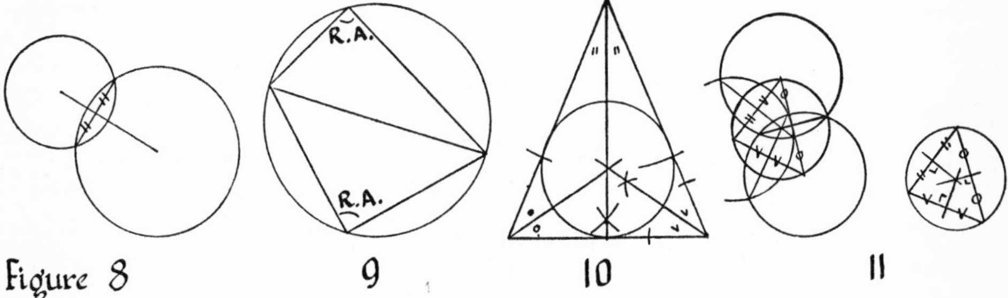

Figure 8 9 10 11

The part of geometry which teaches us about ratio and proportion starts with parallel lines. If you start with a series of parallel lines spaced at equal distances apart, you can divide a line of any length into equal parts (Fig. 1). You also can divide two lines of different lengths into the same number of equal parts (Fig. 1). Suppose you want to divide two lines 4 inches and 7 inches long into 5 equal parts. It is done very easily by parallel lines (Fig. 1). Suppose you have a line that is 9 inches long made up of a line

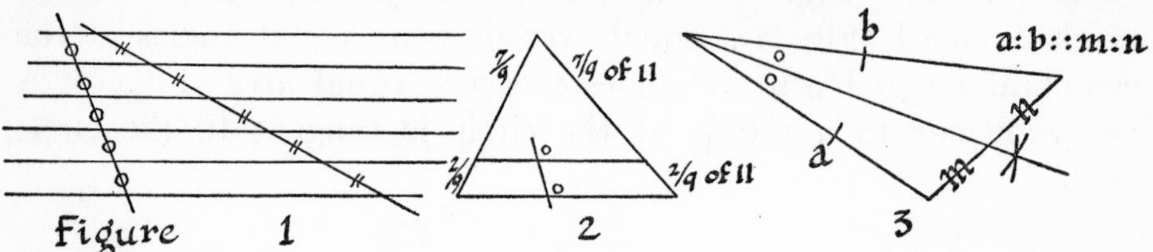

2 inches long and another line 7 inches long. The ratio of the two lines is $\frac{2}{7}$ or 2:7. You want to divide an 11 inch line into 2 parts whose ratio is 2:7. It is troublesome to do it by fractions. Use a triangle and a parallel to the base (Fig. 2). The bisector of an angle in a triangle divides the opposite side into two parts whose ratio is the same as the ratio between the two other sides of the triangle (Fig. 3).

When you drop a perpendicular line from the right angle of a right triangle to the hypotenuse, you make two triangles which are similar to each other and to the original triangle (Fig. 4). The length of the perpendicular line is as much larger than the smaller

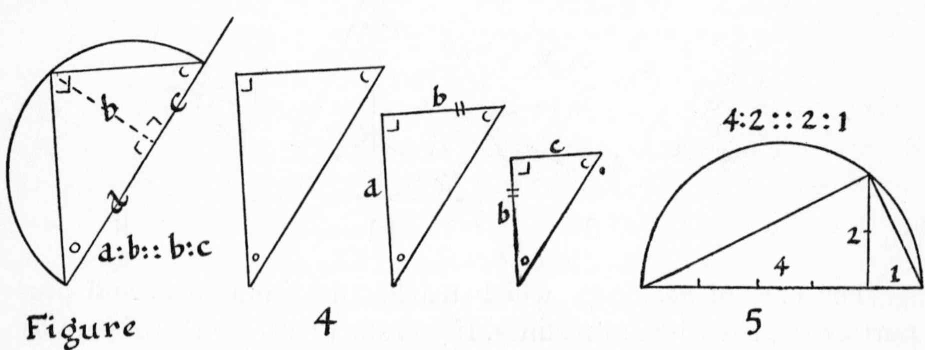

part of the hypotenuse as the larger part of the hypotenuse is larger than the perpendicular (Fig. 5). For example 4:2 as 2:1. In this example 2 is called the "mean proportional" or the "average proportional." You can find the mean proportional between any two numbers by making them the diameter of a circle and erecting a perpendicular where they meet.

Not until very late in the day do Euclid and all the other writers of geometry textbooks tell you something which you and the Egyptian rope-swingers knew from infancy: that the area of a rectangle is equal to the length of one side multiplied by the length of the other (Fig. 6). The reason for the delay is that it doesn't appear in the logical order of things geometrical earlier in the day. Then you are told and given logical proof that a parallelogram's area is also the product of its base and altitude (Fig. 7). At that point you are told that a triangle, being half of a parallelogram has an area half the parallelogram (Fig. 8). Very complicated, isn't it? Not practically but logically.

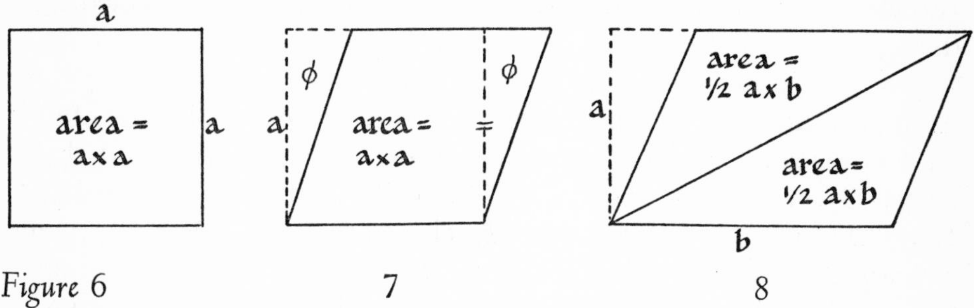

Figure 6 7 8

Then geometry becomes somewhat artistic. It tells you how to make 3, 4, 5, and 6 sided figures fit inside and outside of circles. By dividing each side in half, you can make 8, 10 and 12, 16, 20, and 24 sided figures, and so on. With merely a ruler and compass and the hints in the following illustration, you can indulge in some old-fashioned Egyptian Rope-Swinging. The 3, 4, 6, and 8 sided figures inside and outside the circles are easy. The 5 sided figure is tricky; but when you've worked it out, you're "starred."

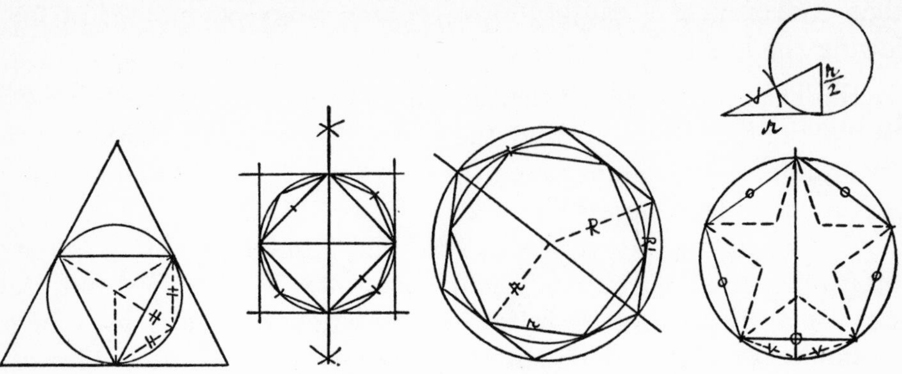

Since we had very plain but nourishing Pythagorean porridge as our first course in geometry, it is only fair to have pie at the end. It isn't very tasty. In the first place it is not spelled *pie* but it is pronounced that way. It is spelled *Pi*. It is printed this way: π.

Pi is a most mysterious number. It is the ratio of the distance around a circle to the distance across a circle passing through the center. In other words it is circumference divided by diameter.

In very early times, *pi* was 3. That was as close as anyone wanted to know it. Six spokes would just about equal the tire of an ox cart wheel. Then people became more exacting. They said that *pi* was $3\frac{1}{7}$. You know that *pi* is 3.1416. Well, it isn't exactly that. It is 3.14159. It isn't that exactly either. It is 3.141592653. You can work it out and out and out to 50 places or 100 places or 200 places and it always keeps changing. Logically, *pi* is very annoying. Practically, it is nothing to worry about. With only those nine figures after the decimal point, you can figure the distance around the earth to the nearest half inch!

One of the many ways to find the value of *pi* is to use geometry. You start of course by drawing any circle and its diameter. Then if you draw a hexagon — that is a figure with six equal sides — inside the circle, you know that the distance around the hexagon is 6 radii or 3 diameters. You can see that *pi* is going to be greater than 3 diameters because you have gone cross-lots instead of following the longer way around the circle.

Suppose we reform. Instead of taking those short cuts, we decide to touch the circle at 12 instead of only 6 points. We find that the

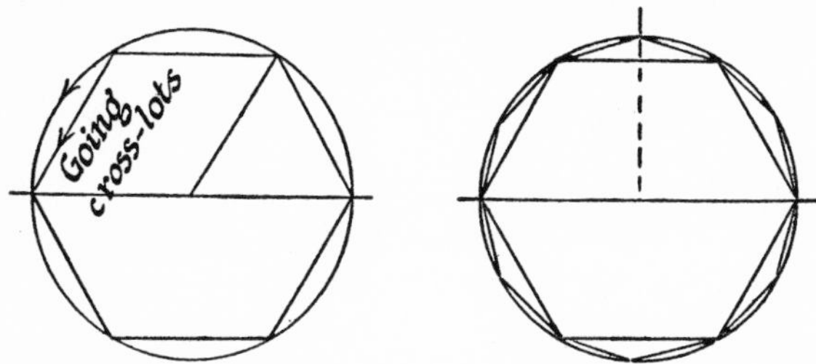

longer path is 3.1 times the diameter. That is a better value for *pi;* but still it is too short.

So we reform some more and touch the circle at 24 points, and then at 48 points, and then at 96 points where we find the value of *pi* is 3.14. When we touch the circle at 192 points our improved *pi* becomes 3.14145. By doubling again the number of points, *pi* becomes 3.14155.

Really it is becoming rather exhausting running around that circle and the reward in the way of corrections for *pi* is becoming smaller and smaller. Although we could go on and on and on, the last trip we make is the one on which we touch the circle at 768 points. *Pi* then has a value of 3.1415847. We decide to stop and call *pi,* "3.1416." We know now that when we roll our pie plate, or any other circle, along the table it will cover a distance 3.1416 times its diameter when it has completed one revolution.

So for the moment, in our romp through mathematics, we take leave of the cult of Euclid, of the discoveries of Pythagoras, and the practical common sense of the Babylonians and the Egyptian rope-swingers. Time and time again, however, their shadows will cross our path and be very welcome shadows indeed.

Long Distance, If You Please

LOGARITHMS

Before the day when the telephone was invented, if you wanted to talk to a friend on the other side of town, you had to go to see him. That took time and meant work. With the telephone, all you have to do is look up the number and make a call. You save time and effort.

Logarithms, too, save time and effort. A book of logarithms is merely a telephone directory of numbers and is of tremendous use in making calculations. The "log" part of the term comes from the Greek *logos* which means to reason or reckon or calculate, and *arithmos* means a number. "Reasoning numbers" are somewhat like trained animals; they know how to do arithmetic by themselves.

Supposing you want to multiply 978 by 369. Each one of these numbers has a "telephone number." You look them up. You add them together. Then you look up in the directory the name of the party who has *that* number and you have the answer, 360,882.

Supposing you want to divide 978 by 369. You subtract the logarithm number for 369 from the logarithm number for 978 and look up the answer in the logarithm directory.

Supposing you want to multiply 978 by 978, that is square it. Or you want to cube it. You look up the logarithm and multiply it by two or three as the case may be and then you have the logarithms of the answers.

Supposing you want to get the square root of 360,882. Well, it's a tough chore by arithmetic, even if you remember how to do it. Divide the number up into pairs: 36/08/82. Take the square root

of the first pair. Square it. Subtract it. Take down the next pair. Multiply the trial square by 20. See how many times that goes . . .

Let's avoid that headache and try it by logarithms.

First we consult the "directory." The log table tells us that the reckoning number which does the work for 360,882 is 5.557365. To obtain the square root, all we have to do is to divide that by two. The answer is 2.778682. Look up the party whose reckoning number is that. Answer — 600.73.

John Napier, a Scotsman, invented logarithms. He put his first

table on the market in 1614. That was just six years before the Pilgrims landed on Plymouth Rock. The lack of religious freedom in England drove the Pilgrim Fathers to the New World and probably spurred on John Napier to work out his invention. He speculated about religion, found that the airing of his views was unpopular, so concentrated on "logs" instead.

Being a thrifty Scotsman and knowing that time is money, he decided that if he could save time, he could save a lot of people both time and money. Kepler, the genius in astronomy who spent most of his lifetime making the computations which proved that the Earth and Mars and the other planets move around the sun in ellipses and not in circles, testified that Napier "tripled the life of an astronomer." Anyway, Napier goes down in the mathematicians' Hall of Fame.

It's always difficult to tell the story of *why* an inventive genius set out to invent what he did. Why did Ben Franklin try to bottle electricity at the end of a kite string? Why did Edison try to make a piece of bamboo charcoal glow in a light bulb in a glass vacuum? Why did Pythagoras try to prove what he did about any right triangle? Why did Napier set out to "triple the life of an astronomer?"

After the job is completed, it's much easier to explain *how* he finally succeeded. Well, these were the tools and facts with which Napier had to start.

He said something like this. (Actually he used other figures which are much too complicated, so simple ones will do.) Take the number 10. Multiply two 10's together and you get 100. Multiply three 10's and you get 1,000. Multiply four 10's together and you get 10,000, and so on. He now had a set of "reckoning numbers," 1, 2, 3, 4.

Real numbers	Their "reckoning numbers"
10	1
100	2
1000	3
10000	4

In other words, the reckoning number in the system based on 10 was just the number of zeros after the 1. The logarithm of 10 is 1. The logarithm of 100 is 2. The logarithm of 1,000 is 3. The logarithm of 10,000 is 4.

He began to multiply and divide and square and extract square roots, using both his real numbers and their logarithms.

He observed that to multiply 100 by 10, you could add their

logarithms — 2 plus 1 equals 3 — which is the logarithm of 1,000, the correct answer.

Could you divide 10,000 by 10 if you subtracted their logarithms? The logarithm of 10,000, 4, less 1 (the logarithm of 10) equals 3. And 3 is the logarithm of 1,000. *It worked!*

Square 1,000. The wind probably was driving the Scotch mist up the glen and made his candle flicker! Log. 1,000 is 3, times 2 (to square it) equals 6. One with 6 zeros behind it . . . 1,000,000. One million! Correct!

The cube root of 1,000,000. . . . Its logarithm is 6. Divide by 3 to get the third root — answer 2. Two is the logarithm of 100. Correct again!

The fifth root of 10,000,000,000. . . . It didn't matter about the stormy night outside. Here was something that man had not been able to do before — extract the fifth root of a number. The square root, yes; the cube root, yes, but more difficult; the fourth root — that was the square root of the square root; but the fifth root — that was something new. By logarithms it was possible.

Logarithm of 10,000,000,000 is 10. Divide the log by 5. Answer 2, which is the logarithm of 100; and 100 multiplied by itself 5 times over is 10,000,000,000.

Here was something that the astronomers would be interested in, those fellows who were wearing their knuckles down to the bone, who had been trying unsuccessfully for more than a hundred years to compute the movements of the planets around the sun.

At this point a terrible thought came to him. It was very discouraging.

All very simple to call 10 by another name, its logarithm, 1. And all very simple, it was, to call 100 by another name, its logarithm, 2. But what about all the other numbers between 10 and 100? What about all those numbers from 11 to 99 inclusive? They would all have to have special names. Each would have to have its own reckoning number.

Eleven's number would be slightly over 1 and 99's slightly

under 2. All those numbers from 11 to 99 would have to have very special reckoning numbers and each one of them only a shade apart.

Who is the person who said, "Genius is an infinite capacity for taking pains for detail?" John Napier should have a middle name and that name should be "Detail."

He set about computing the logarithms of hundreds of numbers. He computed them to several decimal places. It took him months and years. Finally in 1614 when the printers were through with it and the proofs had been checked and rechecked for typographical errors, Napier's brain child saw the light of day.

The illustration reproduced is not actually Napier's first table. It's an improvement suggested and worked out by an Englishman, Mr. Briggs, who was professor of mathematics at Cambridge University. Mr. Briggs was so excited when Napier's tables came out that he rushed straight to Scotland, by stagecoach, since there were no railroads in 1614, to get acquainted with this unknown genius. During every vacation for the next several years, Professor Briggs practically camped on the Napier doorstep. So what you see is just one page from Briggs' tables of logarithms, published in London in 1631. "Chilias I" in Greek means "The First Thousand."

The modern logarithm tables are much more simple and efficient. When you use yours, you will be well repaid for the trouble of learning how to use the telephone directory of reckoning numbers. Then you can multiply numbers by merely adding "logs.," divide by subtracting, square by multiplying, and find square root or cube root or any other root by dividing logarithms.

Chilias 1.

Nu.	Logarithmi	Differ.
1	0,00000,00000	
2	0,30102,99957	17609,12590
3	0,47712,12547	12493,87366
4	0,60205,99913	9691,00130
5	0,69897,00043	7918,12461
6	0,77815,12504	6694,67896
7	0,84509,80400	5799,19470
8	0,90308,99870	5115,25224
9	0,95424,25094	4575,74906
10	1,00000,00000	4139,26852
11	1,04139,26852	3778,85608
12	1,07918,12460	3476,21063
13	1,11394,33523	3218,46834
14	1,14612,80357	2996,32234
15	1,17609,12591	2802,87236
16	1,20411,99827	2632,89387
17	1,23044,89214	2482,35837
18	1,25527,25051	2348,10959
19	1,27875,36010	2227,63947
20	1,30102,99957	2118,92990
21	1,32221,92947	2020,33861
22	1,34242,26808	1930,51552
23	1,36172,78360	1848,34057
24	1,38021,12417	1772,87670
25	1,39794,00087	1703,33393
26	1,41497,33480	1639,04162
27	1,43136,37642	1579,42671
28	1,44715,80313	1523,99666
29	1,46239,79979	1472,32568
30	1,47712,12547	1424,04391
31	1,49136,16938	1378,82845
32	1,50514,99783	1336,39616
33	1,51851,39399	1296,49771
34	1,53147,89170	1258,91274
35	1,54406,80444	1223,44564
36	1,55630,25008	1189,92233
37	1,56820,17241	1158,18725
38	1,57978,35966	1128,10104
39	1,59106,46070	1099,53843
40	1,60205,99913	1072,38654
41	1,61278,38567	1046,54337
42	1,62324,92904	1021,91652
43	1,63346,84556	998,42209
44	1,64345,26765	975,98373
45	1,65321,25138	954,53179
46	1,66275,78317	934,00262
47	1,67209,78579	914,33795
48	1,68124,12374	895,48426
49	1,69019,60800	877,39243
50	1,69897,00043	860,01718

Chilias 1.

Nu.	Logarithmi	Differ.
51	1,70757,01761	843,31675
52	1,71600,33436	827,25260
53	1,72427,58696	811,78902
54	1,73239,37598	796,89297
55	1,74036,26895	782,53375
56	1,74818,80270	768,68287
57	1,75587,48557	755,31379
58	1,76342,79936	742,40180
59	1,77085,20116	729,92388
60	1,77815,12504	717,85846
61	1,78532,98350	706,18545
62	1,79239,16895	694,88600
63	1,79934,05495	683,94245
64	1,80617,99740	673,33826
65	1,81291,33566	663,05789
66	1,81954,39355	653,08672
67	1,82607,48027	643,41100
68	1,83250,89127	634,01780
69	1,83884,90907	624,89493
70	1,84509,80400	616,03087
71	1,85125,83487	607,41477
72	1,85733,24964	599,03637
73	1,86332,28601	590,88596
74	1,86923,17197	582,95437
75	1,87506,12634	575,23289
76	1,88081,35923	567,71329
77	1,88649,07252	560,38775
78	1,89209,46027	553,24886
79	1,89762,70913	546,28957
80	1,90308,99870	539,50319
81	1,90848,50189	532,88335
82	1,91381,38524	526,42400
83	1,91907,80924	520,11937
84	1,92427 92861	513,96396
85	1,92941,80257	507,95255
86	1,93449,84512	502,08014
87	1,93951,92526	496,34196
88	1,94448,26722	490,73344
89	1,94939,00066	485,25028
90	1,95424,25094	479,88829
91	1,95904,13923	474,64350
92	1,96378,78273	469,51213
93	1,96848,29486	464,49050
94	1,97312,78536	459,57517
95	1,97772,36053	454,76277
96	1,98227,12330	450,05013
97	1,98677,17343	445,43414
98	1,99122,60757	440,91189
99	1,99563,51946	436,48054
100	2,00000,00000	432,13738

Chilias 1.

Nu.	Logarithmi	Differ.
101	2,00432,13738	427,87980
102	2,00860,01718	423,70529
103	2,01283,72247	419,61146
104	2,01703,33393	415,59598
105	2,02118,92991	411,65662
106	2,02530,58653	407,79124
107	2,02938,37777	403,99778
108	2,03342,37555	400,27424
109	2,03742.64979	396,61873
110	2,04139,26852	393,02936
111	2,04532,29788	389,50439
112	2,04921,80227	386,04208
113	2,05307,84435	382,64078
114	2,05690,48513	379,29891
115	2,06069,78404	376,01488
116	2,06445,79892	372,78725
117	2,06818,58617	369,61456
118	2,07188,20073	366,49541
119	2,07554,69614	363,42846
120	2,07918,12460	360,41243
121	2,08278,53703	357,44604
122	2,08635,98307	354,52807
123	2,08990,51114	351,65738
124	2,09342,16852	348,83278
125	2,09691,00130	346,05321
126	2,10037,05451	343,31759
127	2,10380,37210	340,62486
128	2,10720,99696	337,97407
129	2,11058,97103	335,36420
130	2,11394,33523	332,79434
131	2,11727,12957	330,26355
132	2,12057,39312	327,77098
133	2,12385,16410	325,31574
134	2,12710,47984	322,89701
135	2,13033,37685	320,51399
136	2,13353,89084	318,16588
137	2,13672,05672	315,85192
138	2,13987,90864	313,57139
139	2,14301,48003	311,32354
140	2,14612,80357	309,10770
141	2,14921,91127	306,92317
142	2,15228,83444	304,76931
143	2,15533,60375	302,64546
144	2,15836,24921	300,55101
145	2,16136,80022	298,48536
146	2,16435,28558	296,44789
147	2,16731,73347	294,43807
148	2,17026,17154	292,45530
149	2,17318,62684	290,49907
150	2,17609,12591	288,56882

The Parable of "Nickels in the Gutter"

PROBABILITIES

Suppose you had twenty coins in your pocket, nickels to be specific. A very oily stranger with a bright red necktie offers to teach you an amusing new game. Here are the rules. Put your hand in your right-hand pocket where the nickels are. Take the nickels out one at a time, and transfer them to your left-hand pocket. Every 5th nickel you throw quite casually into the gutter. Yes, that's all there is to the game. Would you think it was fun? Many people seem to think so, but then they know nothing of the laws of probabilities.

If you did think it was fun, you would see that it cost you only 20¢ to transfer 16 of your original 20 nickels from the right-hand to the left-hand pocket. With the 5th, 10th, 15th, and 20th nickels reposing in the gutter, you would start the second inning by putting the remaining nickels back into the right-hand pocket. The 6th, 12th, and 18th nickels would land in the gutter during the second inning; but you would still have 13 nickels left to play with. But let's read the story in numbers instead of in words. The nickels numbered in the lower of each pair of lines go into the gutter.

"Nickel in the Gutter" Box Score

1	2	3	4		6	7	8	9		11	12	13	14		16	17	18	19	
				5					10					15					20
1	2	3	4		7	8	9	11		13	14	16	17		19	1	2	3	
				6					12					18					4
7	8	9	11		14	16	17	19		2	3	7	8		11	14	16	17	
				13					1					9					19
2	3	7	8		14	16	17	2		7	8	14	16		2	7	8	14	
				11					3					17					16
2	7	8	14		7	8	14	7		14	7	14	7		7	7	7	7	
				2					8					14					7

Wouldn't it be a thrilling climax! Number 7 nickel would go from left to right, from right to left, left right, right left . . . and then B A N G into the gutter!

Does the little parable of *Nickels in the Gutter* remind you of anything familiar?

Of course all of you "dear readers" live in law-abiding communities where the slot machine is unknown! You have never heard from your elders or read in books or newspapers of a place called Monte Carlo where wheels spin and money changes hands. In real life you will never be tempted to gamble; so this chapter on probabilities just may be skipped. Anyway, gambling is illegal.

So is stealing illegal. Yet a great deal of educational effort is expended by parents, teachers, preachers, policemen, judges, jailers, and moving picture actors to prove that "crime does not pay." Perhaps just a tiny page or two might be wasted, then, on the law of probabilities to prove that gambling does not pay. That is, it doesn't pay you. It pays the oily individual who teaches you the game of *Nickels in the Gutter*. So perhaps a brief chapter may be slightly educational and may tend to show that gambling is not only illegal but also extremely stupid. After all, if there were no customers, you'd be surprised at how soon slot machines would disappear. They'd vanish into thin air. Why? Because they didn't pay. Their owners aren't stupid. *They* know their laws of probabilities! Most mathematical truths are found out first by experimenting. Let's do a little experimenting and find out a few of the "Laws of Probabilities" for ourselves.

Please do not believe one single word of what is written down in the next table. Make one for yourself. You probably could work a million years and never get one exactly like this one. It probably would take you a million years to make two alike for yourself. That is the strange thing about probabilities. The evidence is practically never twice the same, but the law itself comes out every time clear as crystal. So make a table for yourself. After all, the laws might be amended by the time you read this; though I doubt it. The one important thing to notice is how to construct the table so that you can make one for yourself.

First start with an idea. You decide on some event which *can happen* one way quite as easily as it *can happen* another way. (Please notice that I did *not* say it will happen one way as often as it will happen another way. It *can* but it *will not*, except in the long run which is its "Probability" of happening.) Well, tossing a coin for heads or tails, picking odd or even numbers out of a hat, or pulling out of your pocket a white marble or a black marble, any one of these will do.

Then number a chart from left to right from 1 to some number like 50 or more, depending on how much time you have. Mark one line "Heads" and the other line "Tails." Then toss a coin again and again and put down each result by a dot on the right line.

After the first toss, which was heads, the percentage of heads was 100%. But after the second toss which was tails, the percentage

AN ACTUAL EXPERIMENT WITH HEADS AND TAILS.

Heads 22
Tails 28
Heads came: 1 1/2 1/3 1/4 5/10 12/20 14/30 18/40 22/50

Percentage of Heads and Tails shown on a chart.
(The dotted line shows tails, the solid line shows heads.)

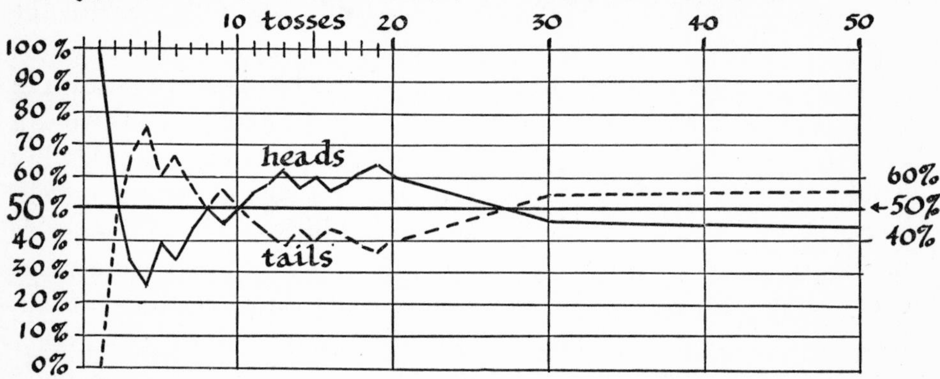

was only 50%. After the third toss it was only $33\frac{1}{3}\%$ and after the fourth toss heads had dropped to 25%! At this point we might conclude almost anything we liked: 100%, 50%, $33\frac{1}{3}\%$, or 25%. But wait; after 10 tosses the line for heads is back to the 50% line. Then it climbs over the 60% line. Then comes a spurt for tails, 8 out of 10 tosses! The line wavers up and down. But the wide swings have disappeared. The longer it grows, the straighter it becomes.

Of course, we could keep this up until we got tired. We could go on to 100 tosses or 500 or 10,000. Probabilities actually should be based on a very large number of tosses. However, if we were forced to guess one line along which the percentage would run, it probably would be the 50% line. But it would never actually stay on it for long. Supposing we actually had made 10,000 tosses and the score was 5,000 heads and 5,000 tails. On the very next toss it would be off the 50% line but by so small an amount you hardly could see it on a chart even if you used a magnifying glass. The ratio of heads would be $\frac{5,001}{10,001}$ and that is such a very small change that it does not even start to jiggle the line. So it seems reasonable to conclude that in tossing heads and tails, heads will *probably* come up 50% of the times in the long run. In other words, when an event like tossing a head can take place as easily in one way as it can in another way, its probability is 50%.

Anyway, let's keep the 50% idea in mind and go on to three articles, a red marble, a white one and a blue one. All of them are of the same size, and if one of them happened to have a rough spot on it so that you could feel which one it was in your pocket, you'd have to wear gloves. Pick one marble from your pocket. Record the result, put the marble back in your pocket, shake them up and repeat.

You may be interested in an actual experiment in probabilities done with three marbles, one red, one white, the third blue. The score rather oddly started out: red, white, blue, then went on red, white, red; blue, red, blue and blue for the first ten drawings. At the end of each ten drawings, the score stood as follows:

Red	4	8	10	14	15	19	23	27	33	36	41	44	45	49	52
White	2	4	7	10	15	18	22	26	28	32	36	39	42	46	50
Blue	4	8	13	16	20	23	25	27	29	32	33	37	43	45	48
Total	10	20	30	40	50	60	70	80	90	100	110	120	130	140	150

To be sure, it looks a bit "fishy." Don't believe anything. Try it for yourself. See if any marble gets more than four points above average. Red in the score above had an exceptional run of luck between 100 and 110, coming up 5 out of 10 times, and exceeded the average of $36\frac{2}{3}$ by $4\frac{1}{3}$ points. But it didn't last for long.

Here is the "fever chart" showing how the law of probabilities emerges when you start with three objects and select them one at a time. Is there much doubt about the line for $33\frac{1}{3}$% winning out in the long run? If not, then you may conclude that the chances of the red coming up is $\frac{1}{3}$, the white $\frac{1}{3}$ and the blue $\frac{1}{3}$.

Percentage of Red, White, and Blue Shown on a Chart

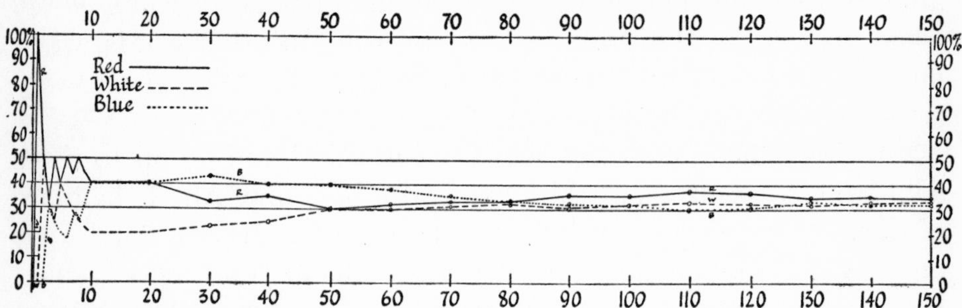

It might be fun to go on and repeat the experiment using four different colored marbles, and then another experiment with five marbles. But we have seen heads and tails settle down fairly soon along the 50% line; and the red, white, and blue marbles straighten out along the $33\frac{1}{3}$% line. All that would happen with four marbles is that they would soon group around the 25% line. The record of the five marbles would show that they soon picked out the 20% line. So we may fairly safely conclude that with *any number* of objects, the probability of its being selected at random is 50% if there are 2, $33\frac{1}{3}$% if there are three, 25% if there are 4, 20% if there are 5, 10% if there are 10, 1% if there are 100, and so cn.

You may have noticed in doing your experiments with heads and tails, that heads came up two or three or four or even more times in a row. There's nothing improbable about that. But it does bring up a very interesting second question. What is the probability of heads coming up twice in succession? Or three times in succession?

It is just as well not to guess how many times heads comes up twice in succession. It is far better to look back at your record on heads and tails and count them. Quite likely you will find that two heads appear in succession about 25 times out of 100. Two tails in succession you will find also about 25 times out of 100. The other

50 times it will be either heads first and then tails or tails first and then heads.

Another way to discover this second "Law of Probabilities" is to take four Jefferson nickels and four Buffalo nickels. In pairs, make all the possible combinations you can. Naturally, it is only courteous to start with President Jefferson.

The coins can be arranged so that you see Jefferson and the Indian, Jefferson and the Buffalo; Monticello and the Indian, Monticello and the Buffalo.

Jefferson and the Indian are both heads and you see heads $\frac{1}{4}$ of the time. Monticello and the Buffalo are tails and you see tails also $\frac{1}{4}$ of the time. Jefferson and the Buffalo, Monticello and the Indian are both heads and tails and you see them $\frac{1}{2}$ of the time.

Still another way to see the operation of the law is this. Your chance of tossing one head is $\frac{1}{2}$. Then half the time your chance of tossing a second head is also $\frac{1}{2}$. So $\frac{1}{2} \times \frac{1}{2}$ of the times you will toss two heads in succession, or $\frac{1}{4}$ of the times. So the law about heads coming up twice in succession is its chance of coming up once multiplied by its chance of coming up once, $\frac{1}{2} \times \frac{1}{2}$, which is $\frac{1}{4}$. So there is nothing improbable about heads or tails coming up twice in succession; its probability is $\frac{1}{4}$.

In fact there is nothing improbable about heads or tails coming up three times in a row, or four or five or ten times in a row. It has happened before and it will happen again. For example, the probability of three heads appearing is $\frac{1}{2} \times \frac{1}{2} \times \frac{1}{2}$, or $\frac{1}{8}$; four heads in a row $\frac{1}{16}$; five heads in a row $\frac{1}{32}$. Now when you expect to see ten heads in a row, you must be patient. The probability is $\frac{1}{2} \times \frac{1}{2} \times \frac{1}{2} \times \frac{1}{2} \times \frac{1}{2} \times \frac{1}{2} \times \frac{1}{2} \times \frac{1}{2} \times \frac{1}{2} \times \frac{1}{2} = \frac{1}{1,024}$.

With the red, white, and blue combination, the same law holds true. The probability of red coming up once is $\frac{1}{3}$, twice is $\frac{1}{3} \times \frac{1}{3} = \frac{1}{9}$, three times is $\frac{1}{3} \times \frac{1}{3} \times \frac{1}{3} = \frac{1}{27}$. In fact there is nothing improbable about red coming up ten times in a row. Its probability of coming up ten times in a row is $\frac{1}{59,049}$. There is absolutely nothing improbable about it happening mathematically; but it is, shall we say, highly infrequent.

Do you know that I believe we've completely forgotten something important? Those twenty nickels in the first part of the chapter lying there in the gutter!

There is no need to hurry back for them, however. The Oily Stranger who taught the little dunce the game of "Nickels in the Gutter" picked them up a long time ago. But he would not stoop so low as to actually pick them out of the gutter. In fact he probably would have a hard time to find many people so stupid as to play that silly game. But when he dresses it up a bit and hides the "Laws of Probabilities" inside a shiny metal box and lets the customers pull a lever and see wheels spin around with cherries and plums and peaches and lemons on the wheels, then he finds plenty of stupid customers. Before you knew something about the law of probabilities, it might be just a little difficult to explain how the Oily Stranger extracted the nickels from your pocket and put them in his without stooping to pick them out of the gutter.

Generally he places one or two of those shiny metal boxes in a store where school children go. There are three wheels inside the box, each one numbered from 1 to 10. Instead of numbers, you see fruit.

Number 1 position on each wheel has a special decoration on it, such as a gold bar. When the three Number 1 positions line up together . . . JACK POT! Nickels seem to rain out of the machine.

But how many? Only about two or three or four dollars worth, at the most.

How many *should* come out?

Well . . . according to the laws of probabilities, the chance of Number 1 on the first wheel stopping in the winning position is $\frac{1}{10}$. The probability of this happening when it happens on the second wheel at the same time is $\frac{1}{10} \times \frac{1}{10}$ or $\frac{1}{100}$. The probability of these two things happening when Number 1 stops in the winning position on the third wheel, too, is $\frac{1}{10} \times \frac{1}{10} \times \frac{1}{10}$ or $\frac{1}{1,000}$!

So, if the Oily Stranger gave the dunces a fair chance, out of the machine when the Jack Pot combination appeared there would pour 1,000 nickels or $50 worth. Instead of that, out comes hardly $5 worth.

Of course the Oily Stranger who has dressed up somewhat the game of "Nickels in the Gutter" pockets the $45. He certainly knows not only his "Laws of Probabilities" but their possibilities, as well.

A Three-Cornered Tale

TRIGONOMETRY

WHAT you can do with three angles to save yourself time and trouble should be the title in English for this department of mathematics instead of "Tri-gono-metry." Of course if you were an ancient Greek, you would understand perfectly that "Trigonometry" means "three-angle-measuring." But why keep up the mystery? The Romans learned the word from Greek slaves whom they imported as schoolmasters. Then the Romans passed on the word, "tri-gono-metry," to the Italians and the French and the British. The British passed it on across the Atlantic Ocean to stare us in the face. About all that can be said in its favor is that one word says it, if you happen to know what it means.

The tale is told in two chapters. Chapter I is really very simple and tells what the ancient Egyptians did with their trigonometry. Chapter II is very practical and tells of the refinements and greater uses to which it was put in modern times. The first chapter compares with the second in just about the same way that the ancient war chariot compares with the modern armored tank. They're related but the modern instrument is much more efficient.

Not only can you save yourself time and trouble with trigonometry but also you can do many things which would otherwise be impossible. But you haven't met the hero, heroine, and villain in the "three-cornered tale."

Mr. Sine is the hero. His co-worker goes under the name of Mrs. Cosine. The "gent" with the long black mustache is Tangent. As the curtain rises they are seated in their respective corners.

The only description of the scenery is that at the front of the stage Tangent is seated before a square corner.

Mr. Sine will always carry two sides of a right angled triangle, the altitude and the slope side, a divided by c. (Now of course

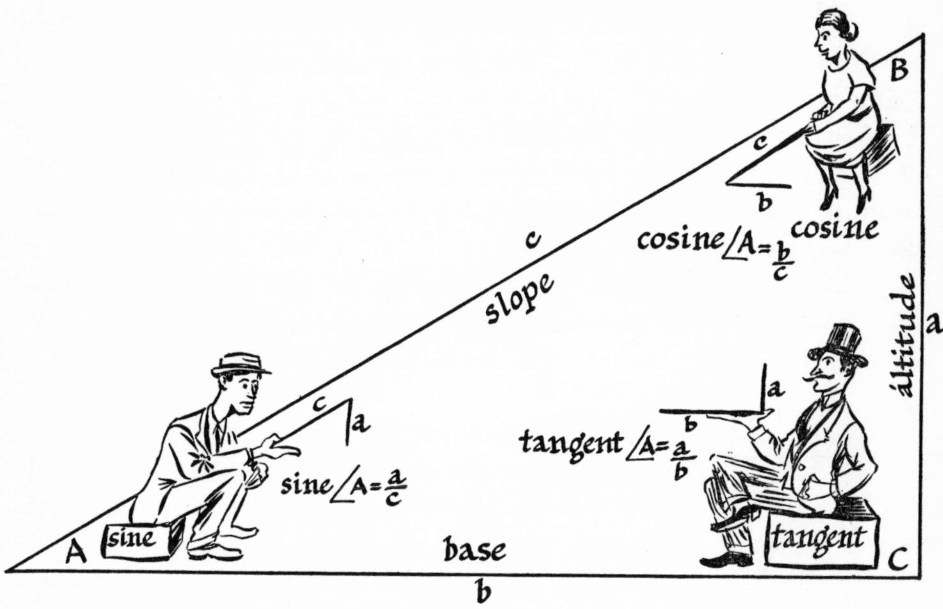

slope isn't spelled with a "c" but that letter is a time honored custom in trigonometry so why worry about spelling?)

Mrs. Cosine, even when she vanishes into thin air, can always be identified because she will carry the base divided by the slope, $\frac{b}{c}$.

Tangent will carry in his eerie invisible hand what is left. You see we have used the slope twice and one altitude and one base and since there are two of each, Tangent has left the altitude which he always carries over the base.

Remember the stage is going all black in just a moment and you will have to identify the characters by their symbols:

Sine of angle A ($\angle$A) is altitude over slope, $\frac{a}{c}\cdot$

Cosine of $\angle$A is base over slope, $\frac{b}{c}\cdot$

Tangent of $\angle$A is altitude over base, $\frac{a}{b}\cdot$

So-o-o-o . . . Flash! . . . Lights out . . . Music . . . Action . . . Camera.

As the lights gradually come on again, the scene is on the desert in Egypt nearly 2000 years ago. Our characters are standing in front of the Great Pyramid at Giza. They want to measure its height. The building plans have been lost. They carry two large triangles. One is made from half of a square board which has been sawed in two diagonally. The other is half of a triangle with three equal sides.

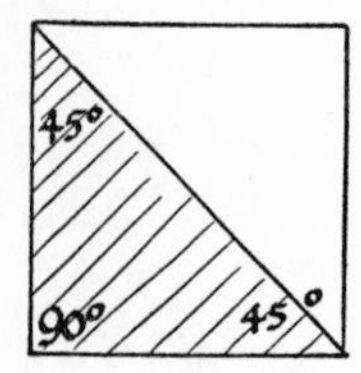

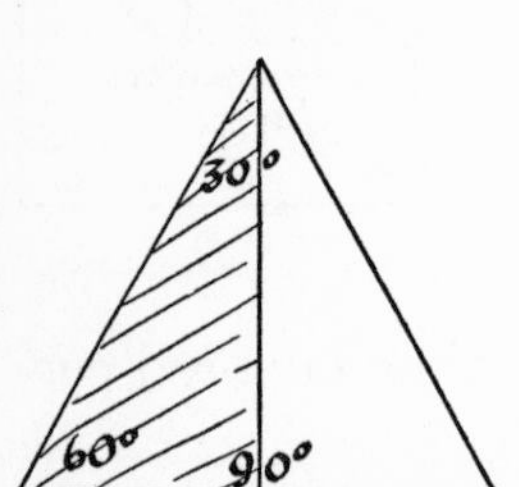

Tangent is doing the work. He walks slowly toward the pyramid along a line at right angles to the middle of its base. Frequently he stops and lines up his triangle with a plumb line.

"Not yet," says Tangent. They move on. Again he sights at the peak of the pyramid.

"Hold on; we've gone too far." Carefully he moves forward and backward, finally coming to a stop in just the right spot. This is what he sees. When the plumb line shows that the right angle is exactly vertical and horizontal, the slope points exactly to the top of the pyramid.

Tangent knows that when he is using half of a square for his triangle, the base is the same as the altitude. So he counts his paces from where he stands to the base of the pyramid, walks to the corner without counting, and then counts paces again until he reaches the middle of the second side. It comes out 160 paces and that is the height of the pyramid.

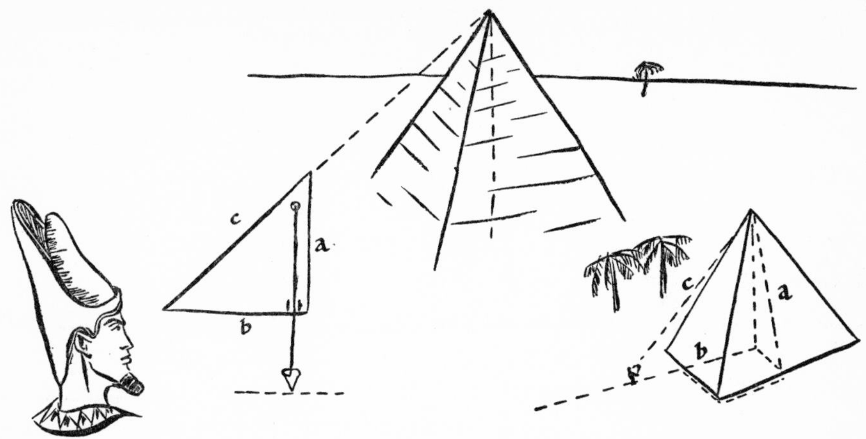

If you don't think that a little trigonometry saves a lot of time and trouble, just figure out how better to do it. Dig a hole from the top to the bottom of the pyramid or build a scaffold at one side as high as the pyramid, so that you could measure it with a string?

Tangent of 45° is altitude divided by base, $\frac{a}{b}$, or $\frac{1}{1}$. The altitude is the same as the base. So if you can measure the base, you can find out the altitude.

The next scene is on the banks of the Nile. The Egyptian surveying party is making its way home for the night. Their village is across the river on the east bank. Some discussion arises about the width of the Nile.

Of course they could have measured its width in much the same way as they had measured the height of the pyramid by using Tangent's two-sides-of-a-square triangle. They would go up to the river bank, point the base straight across the river at a certain palm tree and then look along the slope and pick out a second palm tree, cross the river, and pace off the Nile's width on dry land.

"But just suppose," said Tangent, "that we couldn't go across the river to pace it off."

"Well, you could always turn your triangle around and pace

the width off on this side of the river," said Mrs. Cosine who was still very pleased that they had not been forced to climb to the top of the pyramid.

"I'm getting tired of extra walking," said the lazy villain, Tangent. "In fact I've had almost enough for today. I want to

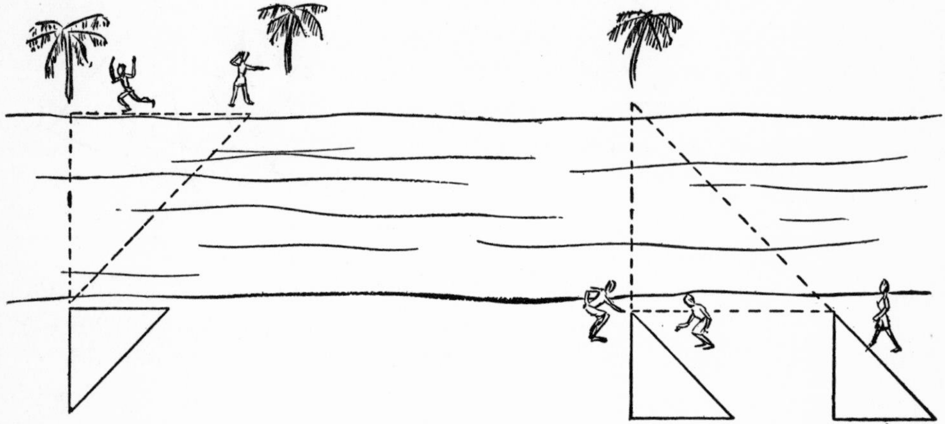

save steps and I know how to do it." The river was still a few hundred yards away.

"You see that tall palm tree straight across the river in front of us?"

"Certainly," said the other two.

"Well, you two stay here. I'll go ahead with the half of the square cut diagonally to make a 45° triangle. You stay here with the 30° and 60° triangle, the one made by cutting a triangle with three equal sides into two duplicate triangles.

"When I get to the bank of the river," Tangent continued, "I'll point the base of my 45° triangle at that first palm tree. Then I'll take a sight along the slope of my triangle and pick out another palm tree down the river. It will be somewhere on that little hill. I'll shout back very loud which one it is, like the second or third or fourth tree.

"Then you point the base of your 30°–60° triangle at the *first* palm tree we picked out directly across the river. Keep on walking slowly until you see the other one on the hill when you sight along your *slope!* Be very certain that you see the first palm tree along the base of your 30°–60° triangle and the other palm tree along the slope! Then you walk straight toward me and count your paces."

Everything worked out according to plan. Here is what lazy Tangent knew, so that he could save extra steps. He knew that the two palm trees across the Nile would be the width of the river apart, because the tangent of 45° is $\frac{100}{100}$. He knew that the tangent of 30° is $\frac{1}{\sqrt{3}}$ or $\frac{100}{173}$.

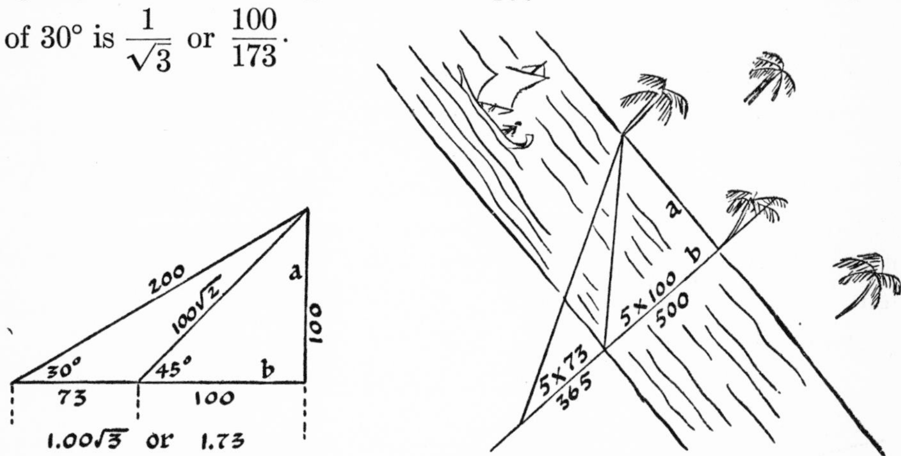

So for every 73 paces that were measured off to reach the river, the Nile would be 100 paces wide. Actually 365 paces were measured off to reach the river bank. So 365 ÷ 73 = 5, which made the Nile 500 paces across at that point. The only thing is, you couldn't possibly pace off the distance without being able to walk on water, and *swimming* is such a poor way to measure distance especially with the current carrying you downstream!

As Mr. Sine, Mrs. Cosine, and Tangent sail home across the Nile and disappear from sight, it is well worthwhile to remember that people in ancient times even with very crude instruments had begun to use their heads instead of their feet. That's not a really bad idea even for modern times. By using the tangent of one angle, you can measure the height of something you can walk up to. By using the tangents of two angles, you can measure something beyond your reach.

Chapter II in "The Three-Cornered Tale" starts with the use of better instruments to measure angles. Ancient peoples did not have telescopes and accurate surveying instruments. They had to get along with very few angles in their trigonometry. But as men developed their mechanical skill, they were able to measure all the angles they wanted to. They needed sines, cosines, and tangents to use with these angles. When they worked out the tables of sines, cosines, and tangents for all the angles they could possibly use, they had taken the great forward step which separated ancient from modern trigonometry.

First, let's try to make a better trigonometry "telephone book," than the ancients had. A trigonometry table is only a special sort of telephone directory which enables us to call more numbers for help when we need it. So far, what we have is a crude telephone book like this:

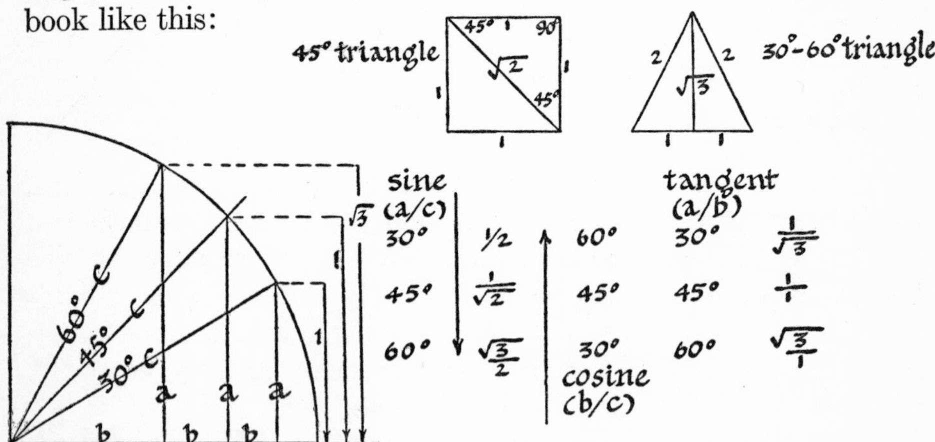

Now let's take the first modern step forward and introduce the decimal system, which is an improvement in arithmetic, making the table easier to use.

(We should not lose sight of the fact that two angles which add up to 90° have the same values for sine and cosine. For example

	sine	cosine	tangent
30°	.50	.87	.58
45°	.71	.71	1.00
60°	.87	.50	1.73

$\frac{1}{2}$ is the sine of 30° and cosine of 60°, although in the decimal system table you have to look in two places to see it.)

Now in order to make an even better trigonometry "telephone book," let's start with a line 100 units long and draw angles every 10°. The slope which we still shall call c will always be 100 in the denominator of our fractions so we can write the sines and cosines in decimals right away. For example in the 10° angle, the altitude a is 17 and c is 100, so a/c is $\frac{17}{100}$ or .17.

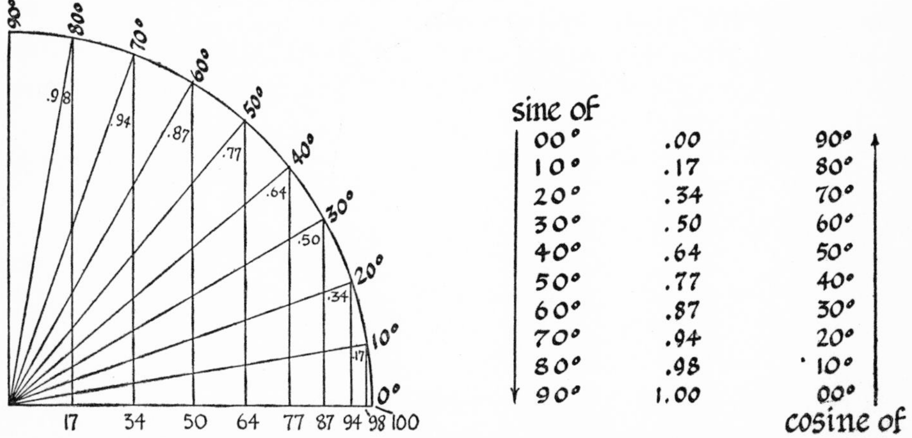

sine of		cosine of
00°	.00	90°
10°	.17	80°
20°	.34	70°
30°	.50	60°
40°	.64	50°
50°	.77	40°
60°	.87	30°
70°	.94	20°
80°	.98	10°
90°	1.00	00°

Of course to get the tangents, some dividing is necessary. For tangent 10°, 17 must be divided by 98, or a/b, which is .17. For 20°, $\frac{34}{94}$ is .36; for 30°, $\frac{50}{87}$ is .58; for 40°, $\frac{64}{77}$ is .84; for 50°, $\frac{77}{64}$ is 1.19; for 60°, $\frac{87}{50}$ is 1.74; for 70°, $\frac{94}{34}$ is 2.75; for 80°, $\frac{98}{17}$ is 5.67. So we can add those tangent values to our table for sines, cosines, and tangents.

Now with our homemade equipment, a table of sines, cosines, and tangents, let's go out and play that we are George Washingtons. I don't mean that groundless fable about George chopping down a young cherry tree. I mean surveying, for that is the way the Father of Our Country started on his road to the Presidency. Only instead of taking along a sharp hatchet, we'll take along a piece of cardboard on which 90° has been marked off in divisions of 10°.

The imaginary piece of land to be surveyed is in the country, although a city park or a large vacant lot would do equally well for a practice survey when you feel inclined to use your trigonometry. The property runs along the road for 250 yards, which we measure by pacing it off. Then we come to the house. At the

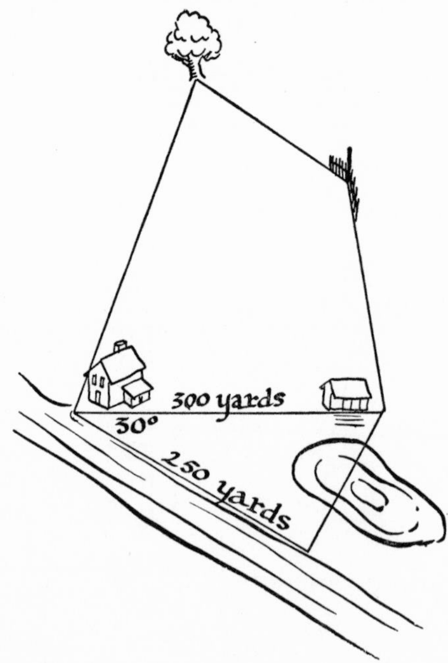

house, a lane cuts back at a 30° angle to the boathouse on the lake. We measure that 30° angle. We can see a tall oak tree which marks the north boundary of the property and a fence post which marks the northeast corner. At the corner near the house we measure the angle between the boathouse and the fence post, 40°; between the fence post and the oak tree, 30°. We pace off the distance from the house to the boathouse and find that it is 300 yards. There at the boathouse we measure the angle between the house on the main road and the oak tree, 60°; between the fence post and the oak tree, 20°.

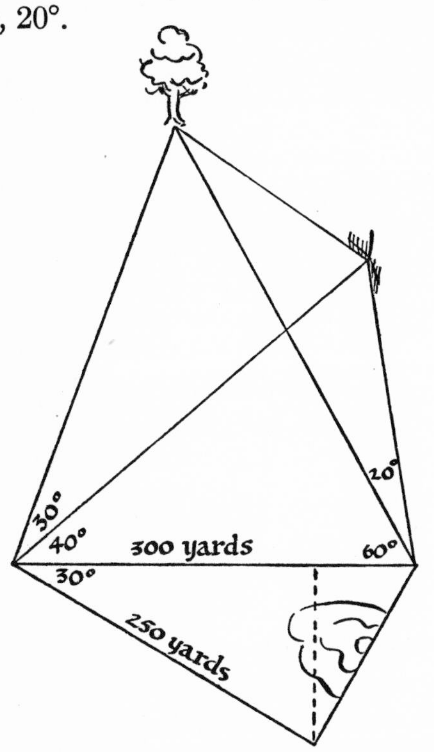

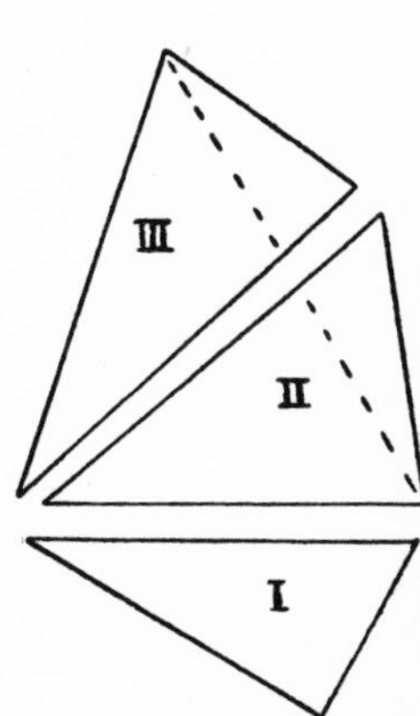

As you see, it is quite an irregular piece of property. What a complicated job it would be if we tried to cut it up into square yards using the methods of Greek geometry and Egyptian rope-swingers! We'd be all day doing it, and probably would stay awake half the night trying to fit in all the irregular bits left over. Besides, what a nuisance it would be to stretch a string across the lake!

With only these few notes on angles and distances, we go into the house to complete our survey, instead of plodding around in the mud and cold outside. These notes enable us to finish our "Three-Cornered Tale" concerning that particular survey, instead of being forced to use our feet, heads, and hands, and considerable patience, in finding out the acreage of this irregular country place.

Seated comfortably at a table indoors instead of rowing a boat across the lake, we arrange our notes and place them on a diagram. Here is what we have. It is quite easy to see that we know the most about Triangle I, less about Triangle II, and practically nothing about Triangle III. So we start with the one about which we know most.

The first thing we do is to draw the dotted line perpendicular to the lane so that we have a right angled triangle. Then we can use our trigonometric table. It may seem a bit strange to call something a base when it isn't at the bottom, but that is what you do because it is helpful. So let's turn our triangle over with the base at the bottom until we get used to calling something a base even though it is on top. The really important distance we must know before we can find the area of Triangle I is the length of *a*.

We might go outdoors and pace it off, but it has started to rain and besides there is that lake in the way! What about calling on trigonometry for help?

The sine of the angle which is 30° is *a* divided by *c* and from the table we also know that it is 0.50 or $\frac{1}{2}$. So if $\frac{a}{250}$ is $\frac{1}{2}$, *a* must be 125 yards because $\frac{125}{250}$ is $\frac{1}{2}$.

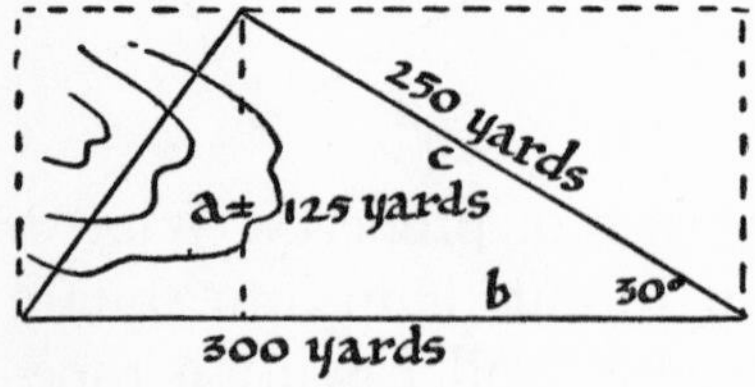

From there on it is clear sailing. The area of Triangle I is $\frac{1}{2}$ of the area of the rectangle which is 300 yards by 125 yards. This works out to be 18,750 square yards. (300 × 125 = 37,500 × $\frac{1}{2}$ = 18,750.)

Now if we were in the surveying business and did that sort of job over and over again, we would get tired of reasoning it out every time. We'd put it down in trigonometric shorthand. And it would read very briefly. "When two sides and the angle between them are known in any triangle, the triangle's area equals:

Area = ½ sine A × one side (b) × other side (c).

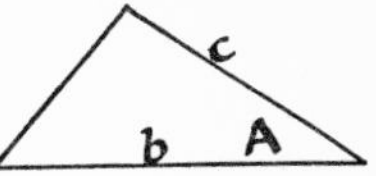

We are now ready to go on and find the area of Triangle II. All that we know about it is that it has a base 300 yards long and an angle of 40° at one end of that line and an angle of 80° (60° + 20°) at the other end.

"In using trigonometry, do you know the Law of Sines?" asks our old friend Mr. Sine from somewhere in the shadows beyond the fireplace.

"No, we do not, Mr. Sine," we reply. "What is the law among all of you Sine folks?"

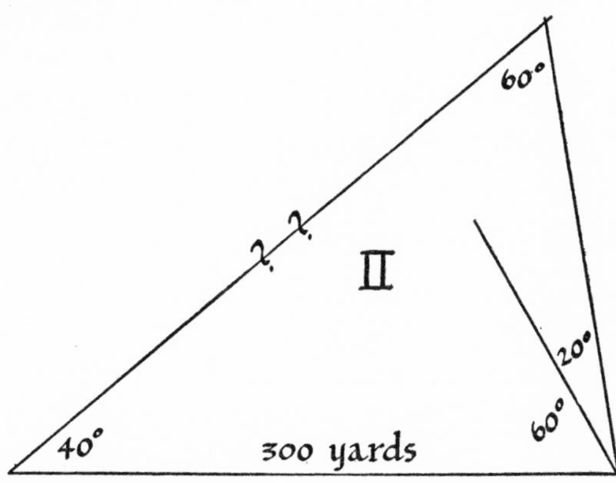

"Well, you seem to be a bit puzzled about how to find the area of that Triangle II of yours," he continues.

"Yes, frankly, we are. We know that one side of it is 300 yards long because we paced it off. Then we have measured that 40° angle near the house and those two angles at the other end which add up to 80°. What we really need to know is the length of that side from the house to the fence post, and it's too cold and rainy outside to pace it off. That is, we'd just as soon avoid doing it.

If we knew that second side, we could go ahead just as we did in Triangle I."

"In other words, if you had some ham," Mr. Sine broke in, "you'd have some ham and eggs . . . if you had some eggs."

We did not mention CORNmeal because old Mr. Sine thought that was a new joke and we wanted him to tell us about the Law of Sines.

"Wa-a-a-a-lll, back there in Egypt in the olden days," Mr. Sine drawled, "my lazy old friend, Tangent, taught us how to save our steps." Then he repeated word for word with a few extras added, the story of measuring the width of the Nile.

We were very patient because we wanted him to get on with the Law of Sines because we thought it might be of some help.

"We Sine folks have had plenty of time to think since those days. We've found out how to save you steps, too.

"Now the Law of Sines says that when you start changing the length of one side of a triangle, you upset the applecart containing all the sines. It's a very serious matter. However," he continued, clearing his throat, "it has one distinct advantage. If you have

the length of one side of a triangle and the two angles at each end of the line, you can actually find the length of the two other sides."

"Very interesting, indeed, Mr. Sine," we commented and were really very much impressed. Besides, that idea was right down the garden lane to the fence post on which we had hopes of finding some ham for our ham and eggs if we had some eggs!

"Just suppose," Mr. Sine continued, "that you were to make side *a* somewhat longer than it is. Necessarily *b* gets longer too. The third side *c* doesn't change in length but suffers just the same, comparatively speaking. Two of the angles change, too. Nothing is the same. The apples are spilled all over the place."

The talkative old gentleman apparently had forgotten to tell us what was the advantage of all this. So we asked him.

"The advantage is this. You know two angles in your Triangle II and one side, 300 yards. Well, why don't you add up the two angles you have. They come to 40° plus 80° or 120°. Subtract that from 180° and you have your third angle."

Frankly, we'd never thought of that.

"Opposite your 60° angle is the 300 yard side. You know the sine of 60°. It is 0.87," he announced without looking at any table of sines. "Well, the side you want to know about is opposite an angle of 80°, whose sine is 0.98. Your 80° angle is larger than your 60° angle and the side opposite the larger angle is larger than the side opposite the smaller angle, and it's as much larger as 98 is larger than 87." He had hardly stopped to catch his breath. When the old gentleman was talking about the Law of Sines, he didn't show his age in the least. Then he cut out a paper triangle and showed us how to find the side we wanted. He just snipped the triangle in two with a pair of shears and did a little simple reasoning. What he said was this in substance.

He called the line on which the cut was made *h*.

sine of 80° is $\frac{98}{100}$ is $\frac{h}{300}$; h is $\frac{300(98)}{100}$

sine of 60° is $\frac{87}{100}$ is $\frac{h}{???}$; h is $\frac{???(87)}{100}$

Since both are equal to "h,"

???(87) = 300(98)

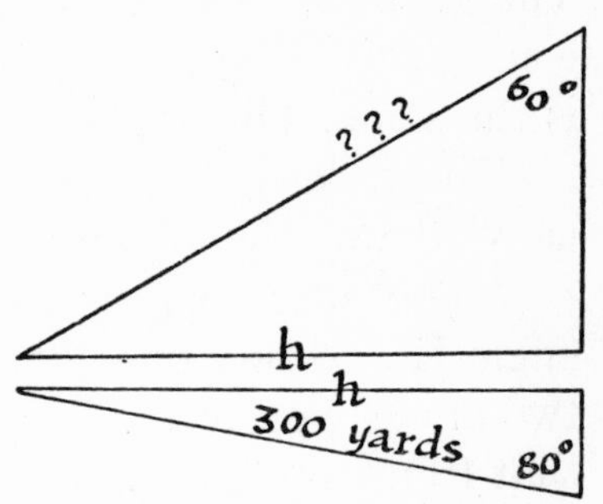

So the side "?" which we want to find is 300 yards × $\frac{98}{87}$; which is exactly what Mr. Sine had said. "It's as much larger than the 300 yard side as 98 is larger than 87." Mr. Sine had vanished so we had to work out the arithmetic for ourselves which we were glad to do, rather than go out in the rain and cold. The "?" side came out 338 yards.

From there on the going was easy. We just used the shorthand which we had learned in connection with Triangle I.

Area of Triangle II is sine 40° (338) (300) (1/2)

Area of Triangle II is (0.64) (338) (300) (1/2)

Area of Triangle II is (96) (338) = 32,448 sq. yds.

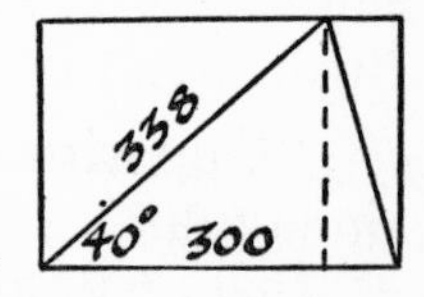

There still remained the upper pasture to be measured. It was Triangle III whose corners were marked by the house, the oak tree, and the fence post. We had never gone any nearer to it than the house. But this is what we knew about it by this time. And since it was dark outside by this time and the cold rain had turned to sleet, we had no desire to go out and investigate, if trigonometry would save us the trouble.

We remembered first the little trick of finding the angle opposite the 300 yard side in the dotted line triangle. It was the difference between 180° and the sum of 60°, 40°, and 30° which turned out to be 50°, which we promptly inserted in our notes. Then we

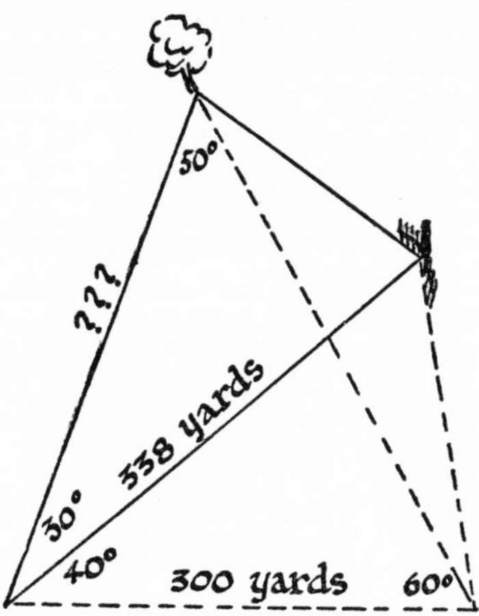

put down what we had just found out in Triangle II, that the distance from the house to the fence post was 338.

Without the benefit of Old Judge Sine to sit on the bench with us while we used the Law of Sines, we said to ourselves, "That '?' side is going to be as much larger than the 300 yard side as the sine of 60° is larger than 50°'s sine." And so it is: $\frac{87}{77} \times 300$ yards. But instead of multiplying out the answer we just save it. We had seen that a great deal of arithmetic can be saved in trigonometry by saving it all until the end.

Using again, "Area of Triangle III is $\frac{1}{2} \times$ sine $30° \times 338 \times ?$," we wrote down the arithmetic problem:

Area of Triangle III is $\frac{1}{2} \times 0.50 \times 338 \times \frac{87}{77} \times 300$
Area of Triangle III is $\frac{1}{2}\times\frac{1}{2}\times300$ which is $\frac{1}{4}\times300$ or $75\times338\times\frac{87}{77}$.

Since it was getting late and we were rather tired we decided to use logarithms and save multiplying and dividing. All we need to do is to look up four logarithms, add three and subtract one.

Logarithm of 75	1.875061
Logarithm of 338	2.528917
Logarithm of 87	1.939519
	6.343497
Logarithm of 77	1.886491
Logarithm of 28,642 square yards	4.457006

That is, the area of Triangle III is 28,642 square yards.

Really, it's quite the lazy man's way of finding the area of Triangle III. With the aid of trigonometry and logarithms, we were able to find that area without ever even finding the second side.

Now we are ready to add up all three triangles. Their total area in square yards divided by 4,840, the number of square yards in one acre, will give us the acreage which we started out to find.

Triangle I (Lake plot)	18,750 square yards
Triangle II (Middle pasture)	32,448 square yards
Triangle III (Upper pasture)	28,642 square yards
4,840)	79,840 square yards
	16.496 acres.

Since we used very rough methods in our surveying, such as pacing off distances, measuring angles with a cardboard marked off in divisions of 10°, and a homemade table of sines, there isn't much use of talking about 16.496 acres. Let's call it about $16\frac{1}{2}$ acres and our survey probably will not be off more than $\frac{1}{4}$ acre.

Instead of measuring off 300 yards from the house to the boathouse on that little $16\frac{1}{2}$ acre country place, let's suppose that we had measured off with accurate surveying instruments 3 miles along the road. Then the points corresponding to the oak tree and the fence post would be 3 or 4 miles away. We would have started a map covering some 8 or 9 square miles. If our triangulation points had been 30 miles apart and our instruments had had a telescope and very delicate means for measuring angles down to degrees, minutes, and seconds, our map would have covered almost 1,000 square miles of territory. Of course we would have needed a surveyor's table of sines, cosines, and tangents. In a professional table, we would have read, for instance, that the sine of 60° is 0.866025 and not 0.87 as our homemade table said.

That sort of table is accurate enough to use in measuring the distance . . . to the *moon*. It is done quite simply by trigonometry. All you would need to do would be to pick out two spots in about the same latitude on opposite sides of the earth, preferably near the equator. At a given second determined either by accurate clocks or by a radio signal, two observers would measure the angle: moon-self-other observer. The two observers would be about 8,000 miles apart if they were near the equator because that is the diameter of the earth. The trigonometry notes would look like this:

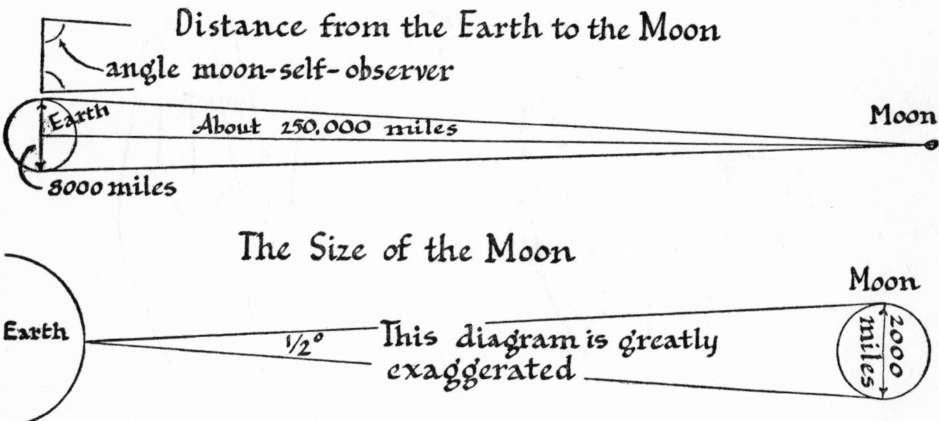

Having found the distance from the earth to the moon, it would be quite easy to find out the diameter of the moon. One single observer measures the angle from one edge of the full moon to the other edge. The angle is about $\frac{1}{2}$ degree. Trigonometry tells us that even that mi-nute′ angle, that tiny angle, proves that the moon's diameter is about 2,000 miles.

By the way, it was during the reign of that excessively gay

British monarch, Charles II, that men were becoming very much concerned over tiny angles. The right angle was divided into 90 degrees. That was all right. But when 1° was divided into 60 parts as the hour was divided into 60 min′utes, they called those "minute′" angles "min′utes." When the "min′ute" was divided a *second* time into 60 parts, they called them "seconds."

Before we leave trigonometry, here is an odd question to ask. Did you know that every normal man, woman, and child has a fairly accurate, built-in, natural angle measuring instrument?

Close one eye. With your palm forward, hold your hand at full arm's length in front of the open eye. At the second joint, your four fingers are measuring 8°! It isn't $7\frac{1}{2}$° and it isn't $8\frac{1}{2}$°. It's very close to 8°.

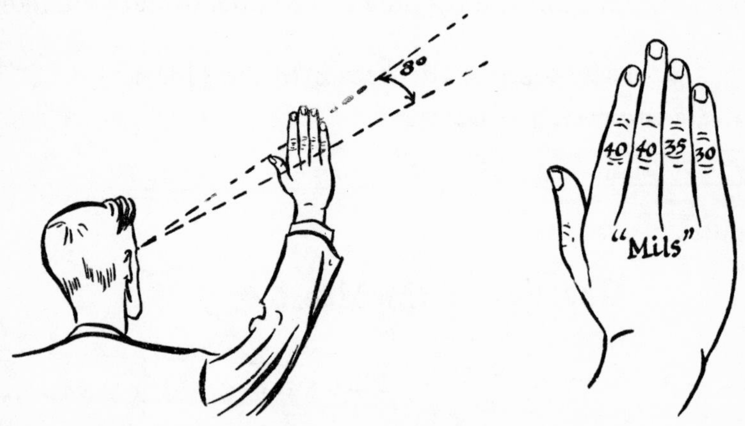

Don't believe it; test it. Measure eleven widths of your hand at the fingers' second joint (88°) and see whether or not it does not come out so close to a right angle that you can't tell the difference.

Degrees are not easy angles for rapid calculation. However, there is an angle called a "mil" — pronounced just like mill but spelled with only one "l" and the word comes from French "millième" meaning thousandth — with which you may or may not be familiar. It is a very handy angle to know about. It measures one foot at 1,000 feet or one yard at 1,000 yards or one meter at 1,000 meters.

Our old villainous friend, Mr. Tangent, might coin a phrase and say, somewhat ungrammatically to be sure, "Yes, sir, a 'mil' is just me when I'm one-in-a-thousand, and a very rare fellow I am at all times!" Well, as a matter of fact, that is exactly what a mil is; it's an angle in a triangle whose base is 1,000 units long and whose altitude is only one unit high.

The reason that it is such a handy angle to know about is that the fingers of your hand at the second joint measure off mils very accurately: the index finger, 40 mils; the second finger, also 40 mils; the third finger, 35 mils; and the little finger, 30 mils. Together your four fingers are 145 mils wide.

Artillery officers use mils all the time. For rough measurements they use their fingers. For accurate measurements, they use the scale in their field glasses. An officer is firing at a target 1,000 yards away. He observes a shell burst 10 mils to the right of his target. He orders his gun to go 10 yards left.

You can use mils in a dozen different ways, and never can tell when they will come in handy. For some reason or other, you want to know how high is a tree, or a building, or a chimney, or a water

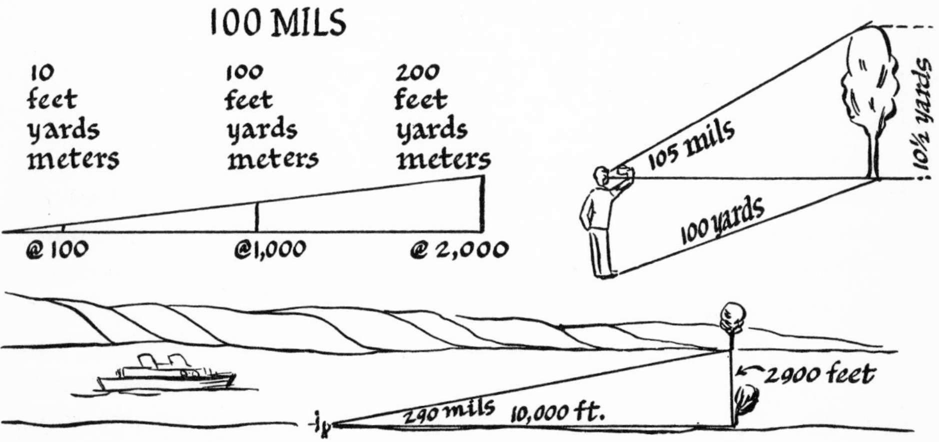

tower. You walk 100 yards away from the tree, turn your hand sideways, measure from the ground to the top of the tree. It is 105 mils. At 1,000 yards it would be 105 yards high; at 100 yards it is only one-tenth that high or $10\frac{1}{2}$ yards, about 37 feet.

"Gee, I'll bet that river is a mile across," someone says.

"No it isn't," says someone else.

You settle the argument. Pick out two trees on opposite sides of the river about two miles upstream. A little less than two miles will be 10,000 feet. The angle between the trees is 290 mils, twice the width of your hand. So the river is 2,900 feet wide, only a little over half a mile.

Rather amusing, and at times somewhat useful, aren't they, our three whimsical old friends, Mrs. Cosine, Mr. Sine, and the sun-tanned villain, Tangent, whom we met years ago on the hot sands at Giza?

Mathematics on the Checkerboard

ANALYTIC GEOMETRY

LET'S try putting arithmetic, algebra, and some of the geometry we already know on a checkerboard. It will open up a door to a room filled with a new, interesting, and extremely useful kind of geometry.

That is what René Descartes did. He put mathematics on a checkerboard. He was a Frenchman and he wrote a book which appeared in print just seventeen years after the Pilgrims landed on Plymouth Rock. His 1637 book was called, *A Discussion of Methods*, methods for using your head in thinking and working. Just to indicate how much importance he attached to being able to think, he said, "I can think; so that proves I exist." What he was saying is that a vegetable such as an onion exists but it doesn't know it because it doesn't think.

The explanation for naming the mathematical checkerboard after René Descartes is something like this. Before Christopher Columbus discovered the New World, Europe ran along pretty much in its old rut. Columbus started a revolution, not only in the current thinking that the earth was flat, that you would sail to the rim of the ocean and then drop off into space, but also in a dozen other revolutionary ways. For instance, there were new countries and unknown people to be found, gold and silver mines to be discovered, rare silks and spices to be bought and sold. The Columbus date of 1492 roughly marks a boundary between the old-fashioned world and the new.

The year 1637 marks somewhat the same kind of boundary

between the old and the new in mathematics. So when you hear the numbered squares on the checkerboard called "Cartesian Coordinates," after "des Cartes" as his family was called before the two words were run together, you'll understand why.

But let's have a look at the checkerboard. At the cross in the center of the board is a point called, "0 — 0."

"Zero — zero!" It is not "Oh — oh!" However, that is what you may exclaim when you see how easily problems are solved on it.

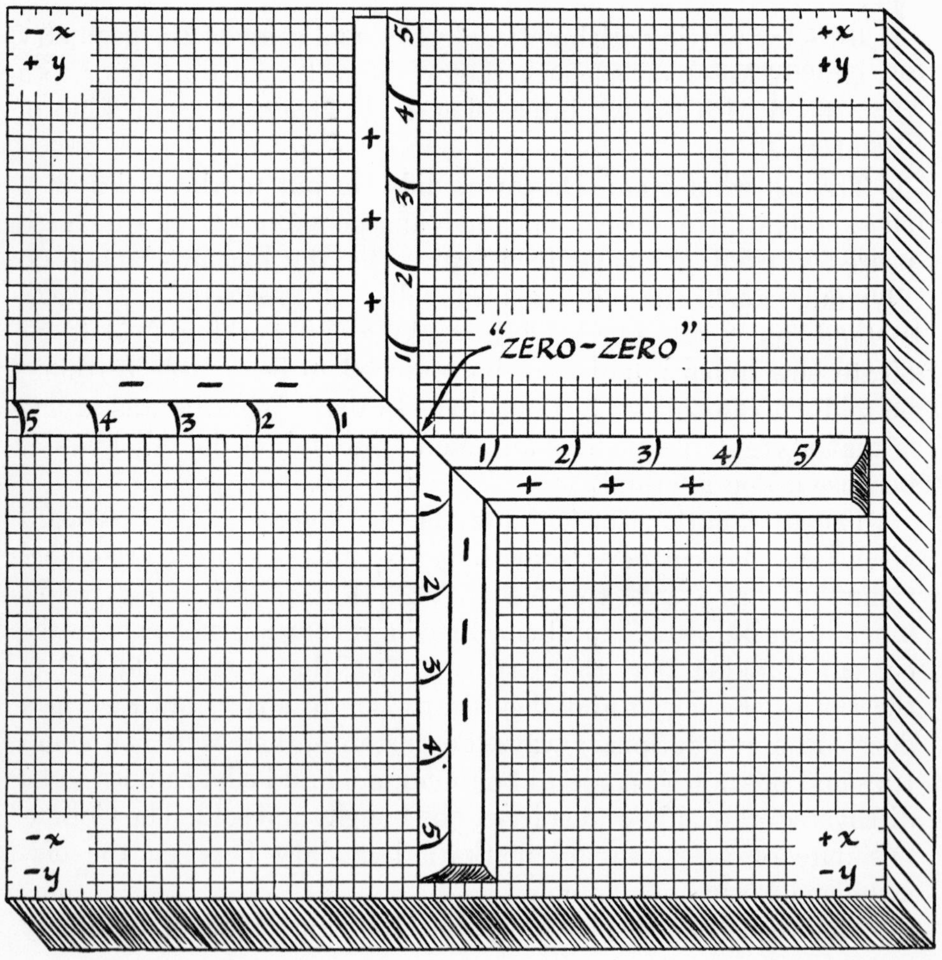

Or you may say, "Oh my; why didn't I know about René Descartes' checkerboard sooner in my life?"

Here is a Descartes Checkerboard. It is really only a sheet of paper ruled in squares. In the center is "zero-zero." Sometimes it is called the "origin" but that isn't important.

What is important is a special four-way ruler which is one of the main features of Descartes' invention. Actually a ruler like it is never used; because once you are familiar with the idea, you don't need a ruler. You do the work in your head.

The ruler which runs from "east to west," using map language for the moment, is known as the x ruler, or rather pair of x rulers. The pair of "north and south" rulers are known as the y rulers. From the "origin," the x ruler reads to the right "plus 1," "plus 2," "plus 3," and so on. From the "origin," the x ruler to the left reads "minus 1," "minus 2," "minus 3," and so on.

On the other hand, the y ruler going north from the origin reads "plus, plus, plus"; and going south reads "minus, minus, minus." In other words, east and north are plus; west and south are minus. An enlargement of the picture at the origin looks like this:

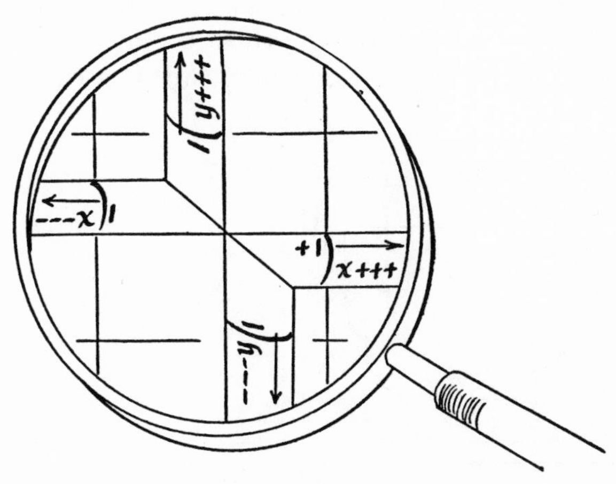

Let's keep the checkerboard, throw away the ruler because it was only an imaginary one anyway; and let René show us how to use the board. First he is going to "do" a problem in algebra for us.

It seems that a mother sent her two children to the store and got into considerable difficulty over the price of sugar and soap. It's one of those typical algebra book problems. Why she didn't ask the children what the prices were and avoid the whole problem never is quite clear. We may suppose that the answer is: if she did that, there would be no algebra problem.

Anyway, the mother sends the boy to the store for two pounds of sugar and three bars of soap, all of which cost 26¢. She sends the girl to the store also (rather stupid that) for one pound of sugar and four bars of soap and the girl brings home 2¢ change from a quarter. How much does sugar cost a pound and how much is a bar of soap? At this point René Descartes takes over.

"Just suppose," he says, speaking excellent English for a Frenchman, "that the soap cost NOTHING AT ALL." (A rather ridiculous idea, but we shall let René have his own way about it.) "*Alors*, I mean, then, the lad who paid 26¢ for two pounds of sugar and three bars of soap — no charge for the soap — would have paid 13¢ a pound for the sugar.

"Now use either ruler you like, the x or the y ruler, for the price of sugar. We'll decide on the x ruler; but from now on we must

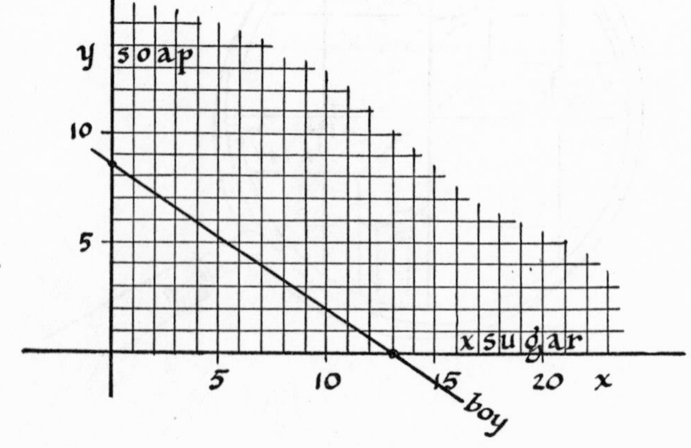

always use the x ruler for sugar and the y ruler for soap. All right, 13¢ a pound maximum for the boy's sugar. Put a dot on the x ruler at 13 for the boy's sugar.

"Now suppose that the sugar were free. Then the boy's three bars of soap would cost 26¢ or one bar, $8\frac{2}{3}$¢. Put a dot on the soap ruler, that is on the y ruler, at $8\frac{2}{3}$. Connect the two points by a line and mark it 'boy.'

"That line you see there is almost a complete pack of lies. At one end, it assumes that soap is free; at the other end, it assumes that sugar is free. With one tiny exception, that line is nothing more than a pack of lies. The problem is to find the one single exception, the point where it tells the truth.

"Have you forgotten about the little girl who also went to the store?" Descartes asks. No, we have not; most decidedly not. What is bothering us is why she was ever sent in the first place. But Descartes is not responsible for that so we are polite and he continues.

"Suppose her soap were free. One pound of sugar would have cost 23¢. Suppose her sugar were free. She then would have paid 23¢ for four bars of soap or $5\frac{3}{4}$¢ each. Put those two points on the graph. Connect them by a line." (Descartes never called it a checkerboard.) So to humor him, we do as requested.

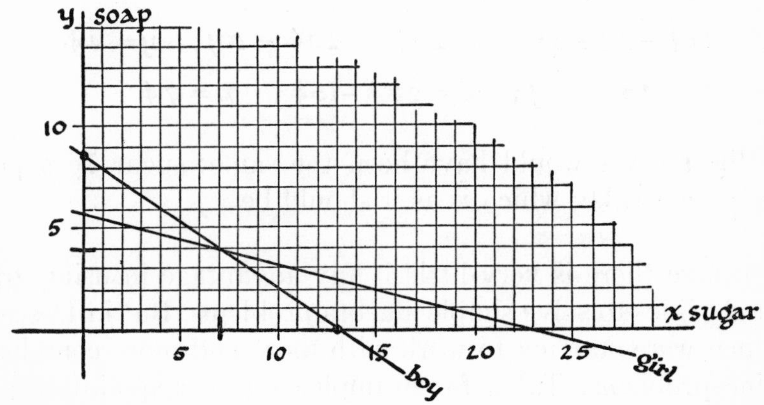

"You see what happens! You see what happens!" René is almost beside himself with joy. Yes, we see what happens. Boy meets girl. Certainly, the lines cross; but what about it?

"Those two lines, so packed full of lies," René continues, "they meet. They meet at one point. They meet at the point where x for sugar is 7¢ and y for soap is 4¢. Where they meet is ZEE TRUTH!"

And sure enough; when we worked it out, those were the prices the worried mother, who couldn't ask her own children questions in the algebra book, wanted to know. Sugar 7¢ a pound and soap 4¢ a bar. The boy's purchases: 2 lbs. sugar @ 7¢, 14¢; 3 soap @ 4¢, 12¢; total 26¢. The girl's purchases: 1 lb. sugar @ 7¢; 4 soap @ 4¢, 16¢; total 23¢.

Actually, what René Descartes had done was to put on his graph two simple equations which Mohammed ibn Mus Al-Khowarizmi would have worked out 800 years earlier by algebra. Al-Khowarizmi would have said in his best Arabic, "Let x represent the price of sugar and y the price of soap." Into algebraic shorthand he would have translated: two pounds of sugar and three bars of soap @ 26¢, and one pound of sugar and four bars of soap @ 23¢ as

$$2x + 3y = 26¢$$

$$x + 4y = 23¢; \quad x = 23¢ - 4y$$

$$2(23¢ - 4y) + 3y = 26¢$$

$$46¢ - 8y + 3y = 26¢; \quad 20¢ = 5y; \quad y = 4¢$$

$$x = 23¢ - 4y; \quad x = 23¢ - 16¢; \quad x = 7¢$$

So the answer would have been the same: sugar 7¢ a pound and soap 4¢ a cake; which is as it should be.

Of course there is very little if any advantage in using graphs of straight lines to solve simple algebra problems. But in Descartes' time, men were starting to work with more and more complicated scientific problems. Take, for example, a new acquaintance who does quite unexpected things in quite unusual places. We are to see quite a bit of him. His name is Galileo.

For thousands of years, the hours of the day had been measured by sundials, and the hours of the night had been measured by water-clocks, running sand in hour glasses, or candles marked to show the passage of time. During the hundred years which followed the voyages of Columbus to the New World, sailors had ventured out on all the oceans of the world. The measurement of time was becoming of greater and greater importance to them. Men were also studying the movement of the moon, planets and stars. That called for the better measurement of time. Yet it was not until Galileo, born in the Italian city of Pisa in 1564, had discovered the pendulum's law, that men were able to start to measure time accurately.

Everyone is so used to seeing a pendulum swinging in a clock on the wall now-a-days that it's hard to imagine a world without clocks. Clocks play a very important part in our lives. They do much more for us than getting us started on time in the morning and telling us when to go to bed at night. Clocks help to keep trains from colliding; but then safety signals help also. How would you like to be at sea and know that nothing else but the clock was keeping your ship from crashing into a rocky island? Well, it is the clock which gives the captain his east-west position. He just goes to the bridge at noon according to sun time in his longitude. That is the time the sun casts a shadow on the north-south line which he knows from the compass. At exactly noon, he looks at the ship's clock which is set to give the time in Greenwich, England. That is the point which reads, "Zero Longitude," on the map. If his Greenwich ship's clock reads 9 A.M. when the sun tells him that it is noon where he is, it means that the sun will take three more hours to cast a noontime shadow in Greenwich. Three hours is $\frac{1}{8}$ of a day and that means that he is $\frac{1}{8}$ of the way around the world *east* of Greenwich. It is *east* of Greenwich, because the sun rises in the east; and *noon* moves around the world from east to west. If he were $\frac{1}{4}$ of a day east of Greenwich, the ship would be 90° East

Longitude but since it is only $\frac{1}{8}$ of a day east, its position is 45° East Longitude. Now supposing there were a rocky island in the ship's course which would be reached if the ship's position were 46° East Longitude, and supposing a pea soup fog settled down over the ocean in the middle of the night so that the lookout couldn't see twice the length of the ship ahead, isn't it clear that an accurate chronometer is rather important in your young life if you go to sea? Otherwise, perhaps in the middle of the night when it is too late to do anything about it, you might hear a shout of "Breakers ahead."

We have Galileo to thank for the pendulum and the law governing the length of time measured by the pendulum. What is involved is almost purely mathematics, with a little mechanical skill mixed in. But let's see for ourselves. Let's rediscover the law of the pendulum. But it would be preferable to choose a location different from that accidentally chosen by Galileo for his first experiment.

It seems that he was sitting in church! To be precise, so the story goes, he was sitting in the Cathedral at Pisa. The sermon must have been dull that particular morning, or perhaps the reason for his wool gathering was that he didn't like the voice of the tenor soloist. Anyway, gazing heavenward, Galileo noticed that the great chandelier suspended from the vaulted roof of the nave was swaying back and forth ever so slightly.

"It must be the morning breeze," Galileo said to himself, for up to that time he very distinctly was not thinking of discovering the law of the pendulum. He just was NOT listening to the tenor, or perhaps it was the sermon.

Many people count sheep in an effort to go to sleep. Galileo began in an offhand manner to count the slow swings of the chandelier in a mild effort to stay awake.

"O . . . n . . . e . . . t . . . w . . . o . . ." Galileo counted softly to himself and very slowly for the pendulum was several yards long.

"I wonder . . . I just wonder how many swings . . . back . . .

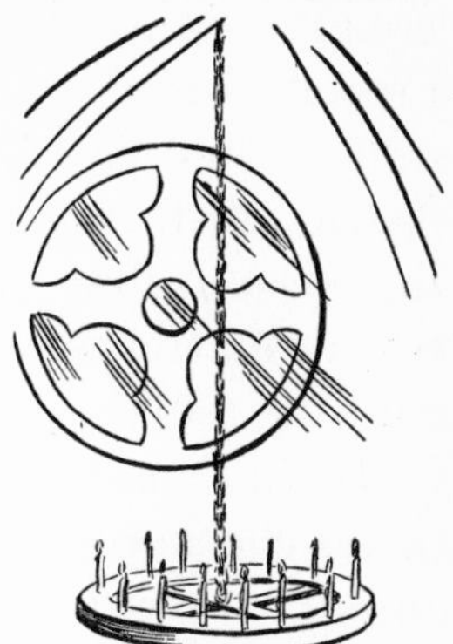

and forth . . . it makes in a minute," he pondered. It was quite a natural question for a man with a clear conscience and so little on his mind. Not having an hourglass handy, for there still were no wrist watches in those days, he was at a loss to proceed. Galileo's great discovery might have been lost there and then.

Suddenly he thought of something. His pulse! No, not his purse, for it was not time for the collection yet. HIS PULSE! He had been sitting there calmly for a long time so his pulse was quite regular, about 80 heartbeats to the minute. So he began to count. Every four heartbeats, the great chandelier pendulum completed, a swing left — right — left. Four more heartbeats and it swung again . . . left — right — left. Back and forth, back and forth. Four heartbeats for each complete swing back and forth.

"Four beats . . . four goes into eighty 20 times . . . $\frac{1}{20}$ of a minute . . . three seconds . . ." Galileo had much to think about. He was very wide awake, indeed. But definitely he was not listening to the tenor. "One-twentieth of a minute . . . it must be a 3 second pendulum. Yes, indeed, *a three second pendulum!*"

Well, after church (or perhaps he waited until Monday, for you never can tell about these apocryphal stories of the great scientists) Galileo went to work at home. To duplicate his work and verify his discovery, all that we need is a piece of string, a piece of metal such as a heavy gold ring or a nut from the hardware — not

the grocery — store, a ruler, a wire paper-clip, and a watch with a second hand.

First notice that a pendulum only three or four inches long swings much more rapidly than one twelve or fifteen inches long. That is the first thing to notice, and the second thing is that it doesn't matter whether the pendulum makes wide or narrow swings, the time remains the same.

If that's as far as one wants to go, there is no need for a Descartes checkerboard. But if you want to find out exactly how long to make a pendulum to measure any required fraction of a second, the graph is necessary. So let's repeat what Galileo did.

First we take a ruler which is marked in centimeters. We tie the weight to one end of the string. Then we put ink marks on the string every 10 centimeters up to 100 centimeters or 1 meter which is $39\frac{3}{8}$ inches or a few inches over a yard. Then we mark off two meters, three meters, and four meters on the string.

Then we write down the time in seconds for 100 one-way trips of the pendulum when it is four meters long. That is the same as counting 50 round trips — a swing from right to left and back from left to right. The time you get should be something like 198 or 202 seconds, 200 seconds if you are accurate, for 50 round trips of a 4 meter pendulum. Then you shorten the string and time the 3 meter pendulum, the 2 meter pendulum, the 1 meter pendulum, and so on until you have timed the fast little pendulum only 10 centimeters long.

Here are the results I found for myself.

When the pendulum was y meters long	It took x seconds to make 50 round trips (100 one way)
0.10 meters	30 seconds
0.20	45
0.30	54
0.40	64
0.50	70

0.60	78
0.70	84
0.80	90
0.90	94
1.00	100
2.00	140
3.00	174
4.00	200

Now you will see the reason for counting only 50 round trips. Since 50 round trips is the same as 100 one-way trips, if you point off two places in your table showing seconds, you will have the time in $\frac{1}{100}$ seconds for the pendulum to swing from one side to the other.

Can you see any law of the pendulum showing up yet in that table of figures? Your eyes are pretty keen if you can. The clues are very well hidden. You know that the shorter it is, the faster it swings, but the question is how much faster.

Call on René Descartes for some help. Plot the results on a graph. Of course the first thing to do is to decide what goes on which ruler. It is customary to put time on the x ruler.

So here is the picture to be seen when the results are plotted.

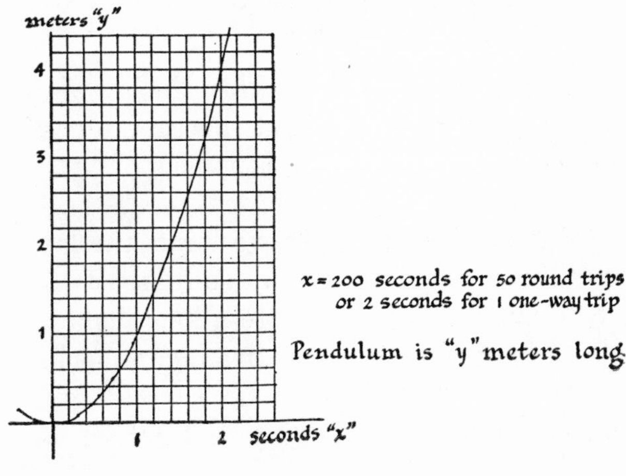

After you have worked with René Descartes for a very short time, that picture gives you all the clue you need to discover the law of the pendulum. You'll say right away, "Why all you have to do is to take the square root of the length and that gives you the time." That first square with the dotted line is very interesting. It should be enlarged. Magnified 3 times it looks like this when our figures are put on it for the short pendulums:

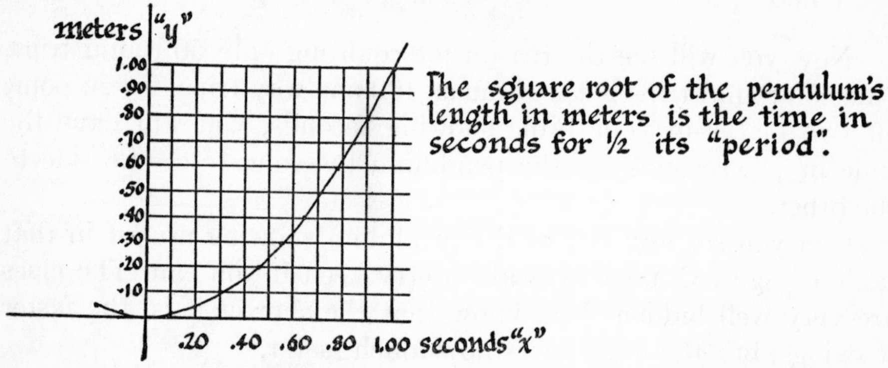

The square root of the pendulum's length in meters is the time in seconds for $\frac{1}{2}$ of its "period."

That curve which we plotted from our figures is called a "parabola" and it has an equation to describe it. The equation is:

$$y = x^2$$

That is a very quick way to write down the law of the pendulum. The length of the pendulum is y and the time for one-half of the pendulum's period is x. A round trip is spoken of as the pendulum's period.

Here is a great advantage: once we know the law, we can tell about any pendulum. The length of a pendulum with a half-period of 3 seconds is 9 meters, which is quite a long pendulum; but so is 6 seconds quite a long time between ticks on a clock.

Galileo was very much intrigued by that mysterious force which kept his pendulums of different lengths swinging back and forth. "Why that is a new way to tell time," he said to himself. "All you need to do is to put a counter on the pendulum and a spring to give it a little shove now and then to keep it going." As a matter of fact that is all a clock is. It just keeps score on the pendulum. If it runs too fast, you lengthen the pendulum. Most of the work for the spring or the weights is to move the hands so that anyone can read the score on the pendulum at any time.

Galileo, and everyone else for that matter, was familiar with the force which kept his pendulum swinging. It was the same force which pulled you down to the floor when you jumped off a chair. But no one had taken the trouble to study the force of gravity. Well, Galileo did.

With the pendulum, he felt that he was rather taking advantage of gravity. He tied a weight to a string, let gravity pull it down a little way; but then he kept the weight on the string and it climbed up hill a little way until gravity stopped it, and then it came down again and the whole thing went on over and over again. It was really being slightly unfair to gravity. So Galileo decided to let gravity have its own way entirely with "no strings attached."

In Pisa, The Leaning Tower was the tallest building in town open to the public. Galileo rigged up for himself a pendulum with a one second period. Its half-period being $\frac{5}{10}$ of a second meant that its length would be the square of that or $\frac{25}{100}$ of a meter. Then Galileo filled his pocket with stones and made his way to the tower. He was going to let gravity have its own way.

He made several tests and finally found that when he dropped stones from the window which was 16 feet above the pavement they took exactly one second to reach the ground. Of course he was careful to see that no passers-by were hit by the stones. But some women on their way home from market thought that he was slightly touched in the head . . . a full-grown man dropping stones off The Leaning Tower!

Then he climbed up to the 32 foot level, which was a very

logical thing to do, and dropped some more stones. They should take two seconds to reach the ground, he reasoned. But they did not. They bounced on the pavement much too soon. So up he climbed to the 48 foot level. But again the stones landed below before his pendulum could tick off two seconds.

It was not until he had gone up actually to the 64 foot level that the stones took two seconds to reach the ground. "Certainly there was something very odd about that," he said to himself. "I just wonder how high I shall have to climb before they take three seconds to reach the ground."

Well, it was on the 144 foot level that the pendulum ticked off three seconds before the stones hit the pavement. There the experiment halted abruptly. He had climbed clear to the top story of The Leaning Tower but the stones reached the ground in less than four seconds.

But we can build ourselves as much more Leaning Tower as we want with a simple sheet of graph paper. Here are Galileo's results, plotting time along the x ruler and distance fallen on the y ruler. (Don't be annoyed by the curve going up. We know that the stones went down; but we are trying to find out how far the stone falls in four or five or more seconds since both we and Galileo ran out of extra stories on The Leaning Tower.)

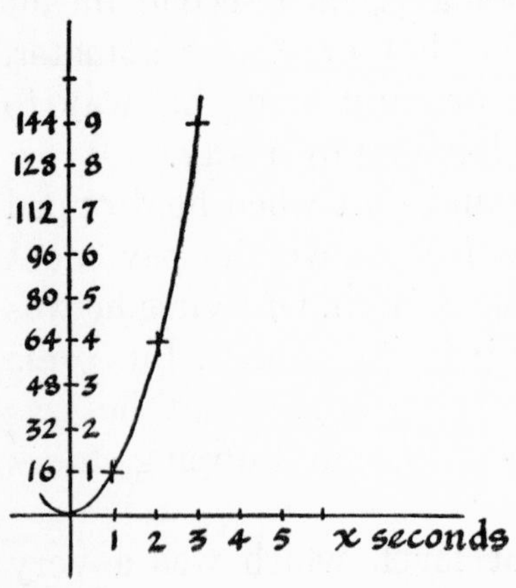

When his figures are put on a graph, you recognize immediately our old friend the parabola. Each y unit is 16 feet, the distance fallen by a stone in the first second. The number of seconds is measured along the x ruler. Square the number of seconds and multiply by 16; you have the distance fallen. So the "Law of Falling Bodies" is: Distance is 16 times the square of the number of seconds. Again . . . $y = 16x^2$.

Oh, if you're still curious about those extra paper stories on The Leaning Tower of Pisa, you can find out how far stones will fall in four, five, six, or any number of seconds. Just use $y = 16x^2$.

When x is 4, x^2 is 16 and $16x^2$ is 256 feet.
When x is 5, x^2 is 25 and $16x^2$ is 400 feet.
When x is 6, x^2 is 36 and $16x^2$ is 576 feet.

It is hardly necessary to go on; for a fall of 576 feet in six seconds flat is quite enough of a fall.

That is about as far as Galileo went with his study of the Law of Gravitation; but Sir Isaac Newton, as we shall read in the next chapter on calculus, went considerably farther when a ripe apple parted from its twig one autumn afternoon. Sir Isaac was reclining under the tree. Gravity took charge of the apple. It made such an impression on Sir Isaac — in the forehead to be precise — that perhaps we owe to the English apple our understanding of what holds the universe together.

You might wish to test the Law of Gravitation for yourself, even though you do not have handy a Leaning Tower. Rig up a 1 second or a 2 second pendulum. Get someone to read the time for you. Then toss a baseball over a 16 foot tree. It will take 1 second to go up and 1 second to come down. Find a 60 foot tree and clear it by about 4 feet with the baseball. It will take 2 seconds to go up and 2 seconds to come down. If you can throw a ball up 144 feet, it will stay in the air 6 seconds. You might try throwing a ball as high as you can and count the seconds it stays off the ground. How high did it go? Time will tell!

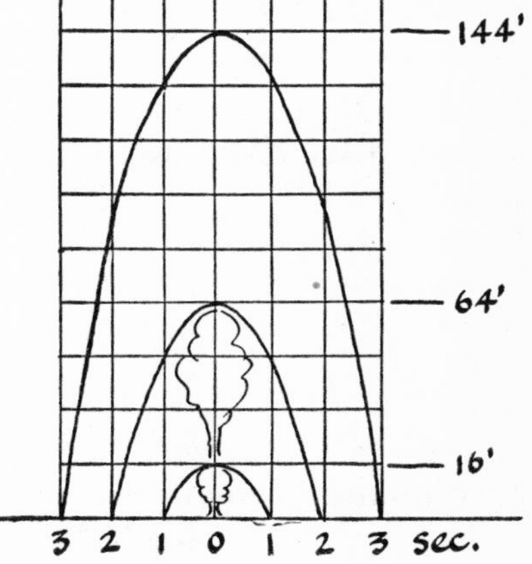

It would be a shame to leave the Cartesian checkerboard without putting two or three other useful curves on it. René Descartes showed us how to do it with straight lines which solved algebra problems. By looking over Galileo's shoulder, we saw that the swinging pendulum and the falling stone put parabolas on the checkerboard for themselves. When you are dealing with only x and y, you get straight lines. But when you square x, as in the equation, $y = x^2$, you meet the parabola.

But what happens when you square both x and y as in this equation, for example:

$$x^2 + y^2 = 36.$$

Before we start making a table of values for this equation, we should notice that the square of both "plus 6" and "minus 6" is 36.

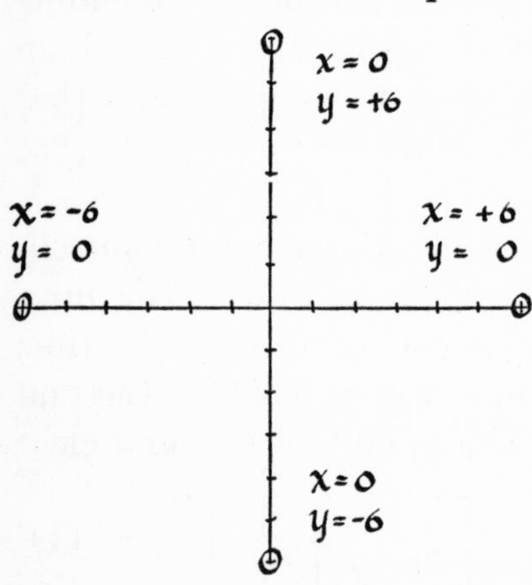

In other words, $+6^2 = +36$ and $-6^2 = +36$.

The table for x and y values in the equation is: When $y = 0$, $x = +$ or $- 6$, which is written ± 6. When $x = 0$, $y = \pm 6$.

So if we put these four points on the graph, we have its outline. It is something which we have not seen on the plotting board before. Quite confidentially, a compass has always been necessary to draw it.

But if we go on, we find that when x is ± 1, y is $\pm \sqrt{35}$

when x is ± 2, y is $\pm \sqrt{32}$

when x is ± 3, y is $\pm \sqrt{27}$

when x is ± 4, y is $\pm \sqrt{20}$

when x is ± 5, y is $\pm \sqrt{11}$

Similarly, when y is ± 1, ± 2, ± 3, ± 4, and ± 5;

x is ± 5.9, ± 5.7, ± 5.2, ± 4.5, and ± 3.3.

This gives us 44 different points. Maybe it seems like a great deal of work in arithmetic, but when we finish it, we have found a new way to draw a circle. In the past we have always needed a compass to draw a circle. Now by plotting the values for x and y in the equation,

$$x^2 + y^2 = 36,$$

we find that we have a circle whose radius is $\sqrt{36}$.

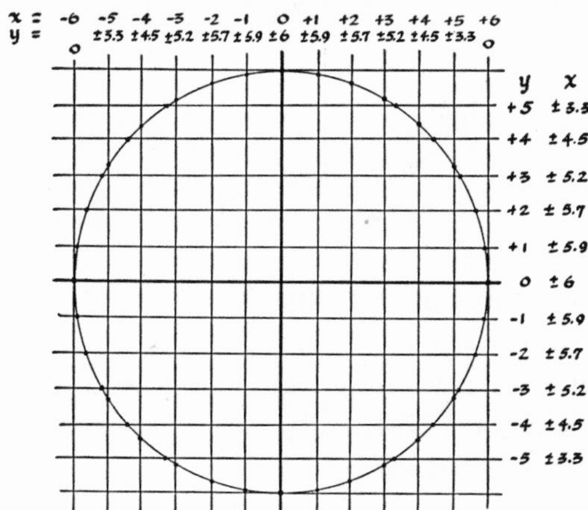

So our definition of a circle is no longer limited to the one which we learned with the Greeks, "A circle is the curved line bounding part of a plane, all of whose points are equally distant from a point called the center." Descartes says that a circle is made up of all the values of x and y whose squares add up to a given number.

For example, here is a circle whose radius is 1 inch or 1 mile or 1 yard or 1 meter or 1 kilometer or 1 of anything else:

$$x^2 + y^2 = 1$$

Here is the equation of a circle whose radius is 2 units of anything:

$$x^2 + y^2 = 4$$

And here is the equation of a circle whose radius is 9,000 miles:

$$x^2 + y^2 = 81{,}000{,}000$$

Descartes' checkerboard will take circles as large as you care to make them, and save you an enormous amount of work in dealing with them.

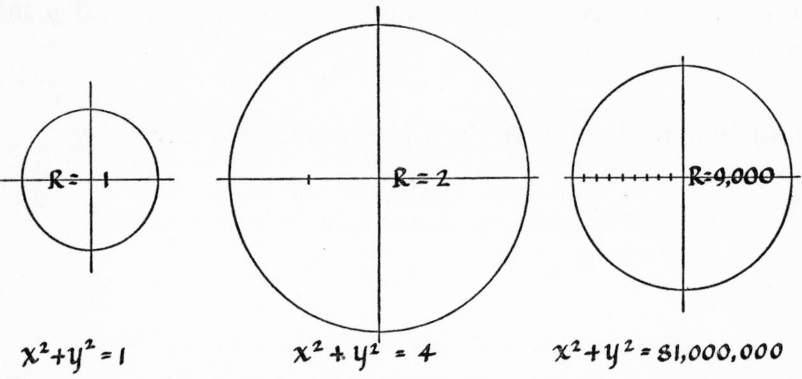

An ellipse is a most intriguing figure. Like a circle, an ellipse has a center. Unlike a circle, it does not have a radius. Instead it has a major axis, that is its long dimension, and a minor axis, which is its short dimension. Naturally, an ellipse is very difficult to draw. Here is the way to do it.

We want to draw an ellipse with 10 for its major axis and 6 for its minor axis. Divide both by 2. Square both 5 and 3. Subtract the 9 from the 25. Take the square root of the 16 remaining. It is 4. Push two pins through the paper twice that distance apart and draw the ellipse with a pencil and string as indicated.

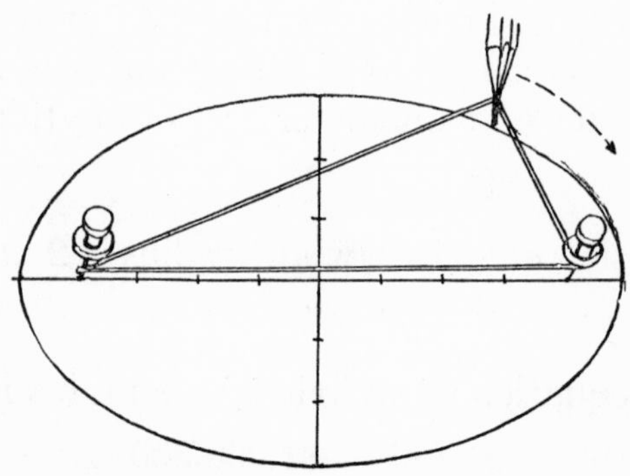

In the language of Descartes, that same ellipse has this for its equation:

$$\frac{x^2}{(5)^2} + \frac{y^2}{(3)^2} = 1 \quad \text{or} \quad \frac{x^2}{25} + \frac{y^2}{9} = 1$$

The table of values for $\pm x$ and $\pm y$ are:

When x is 0, ± 1, ± 2, ± 3, ± 4, ± 5;

y is ± 3, ± 2.9, ± 2.7, ± 2.4, ± 1.8, 0.

When y is 0, ± 1, ± 2, ± 3;

x is ± 5, ± 4.7, ± 3.7, 0.

When these figures are placed on the graph, this is the way they look. Just as it is possible to draw a circle without a compass, so is it possible to draw an ellipse without two pins and a string.

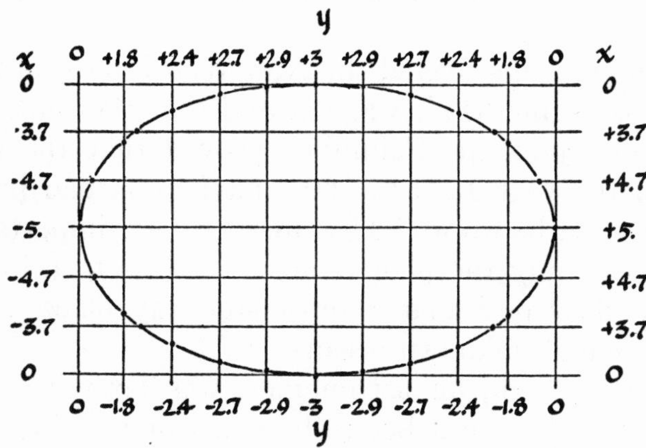

The circle, the ellipse, the parabola, and the hyperbola all are curves which may be found by slicing through a cone. To make the cone, you turn a right triangle around on its altitude through 360°. The plane of the circle is always parallel to the base of the cone. The plane of the parabola is always parallel to the side of the cone. The angle made by the plane of the ellipse with the base is always a smaller angle than the angle made by the parabola; if it is a larger angle, the curve becomes an hyperbola.

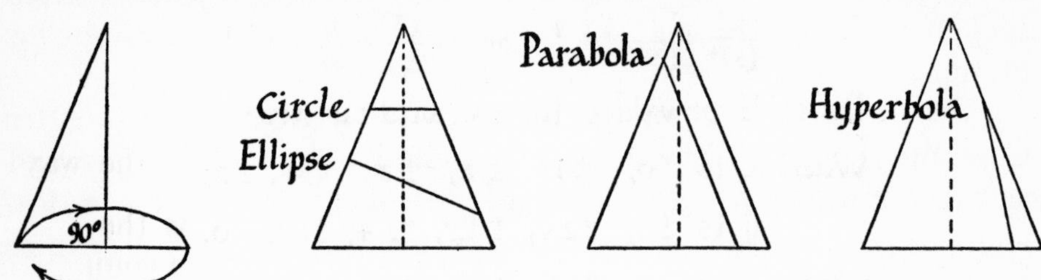

Among the first workers to join the Descartes cheering section were the astronomers. They have to deal with figures of "astronomical" size. Computations take up most of their time. A very difficult problem presented itself to one of the astronomers. But to see what the shooting was all about, it will be well to recall just what the ideas about astronomy were at this time for they were changing very rapidly.

Until Columbus discovered the New World, most of the people in the world thought that it was flat and that the sun, moon, and stars revolved around it. Columbus proved that the world was round. From the year 1500 to 1600, navigators had been sailing literally "all over the world." That made it very important for the astronomers to study the planets and the stars to help the navigators locate their positions in out-of-the-way places and in the middle of wide and unknown oceans.

Niklas Koppernigk, an astronomer, was born in Thorn, Poland, in 1473. He wrote a book about astronomy just before he died in 1543. Radical was not the word for what was in that book. He said very flatly that the sun, planets and stars do *not* revolve around the earth. He said that the sun *stands still* and that the earth and the other planets of the sun move in circles around the sun!

"What was the world coming to?" shouted thousands of good people, the kind however who do not really think for themselves but merely shift their prejudices now and then. "Columbus proves the world is round. And now this Polish upstart says that the earth moves around the sun." Nicolaus Copernicus, as he is more often spoken of by his Latin name, really created quite a stir in his lifetime.

Tycho Brahe was born in Denmark in 1546, three years after Copernicus died. Tycho Brahe had to study mathematics and astronomy secretly, because his father wanted him to be a statesman. He was always getting into scrapes, not only with his father for "wasting his time on mathematics and the stars," but also with several other people. In one of his worst scrapes, he got into a duel and had his nose cut off. So he just wore a brass nose all the rest of his life.

But nose or no nose, the King of Denmark built him a castle-observatory which was equipped with the most delicate instruments of that day. Tycho studied the movements of the stars for 20 years. Then the king died. The next king thought that 20 years of star gazing was enough for Tycho and would give him no more money. So another king, Rudolph of Bohemia, gave him another observatory to work in near Prague. In 1601 Tycho Brahe died, leaving huge piles and piles of notebooks filled with figures on the positions of the stars and planets.

One of Tycho's young assistants was John Kepler, a brilliant Würtemberger, born in 1571. Kepler wasn't allowed to go on working in the Prague observatory, but he was allowed to work over Tycho Brahe's figures. After all, what harm could come from letting him have a pile of meaningless figures?

But we were speaking about circles on the checkerboard, weren't we? Then why all this talk about Niklas, Tycho, and John?

Well, John was sure that Tycho was an exceedingly careful and accurate worker. John spent several years plotting Tycho's figures, especially those which gave the positions of the planet, Mars. Copernicus said that Mars moved in a circle around the sun. On a circle, however, darned old Mars always showed up about eight minutes late! Not by the clock. On the checkerboard!! Eight minutes is such a small angle, less than $\frac{1}{7}$ of 1°, that you must excuse the artist if he exaggerates a bit to show the discovery which made it possible for you to know the truth about how the universe works.

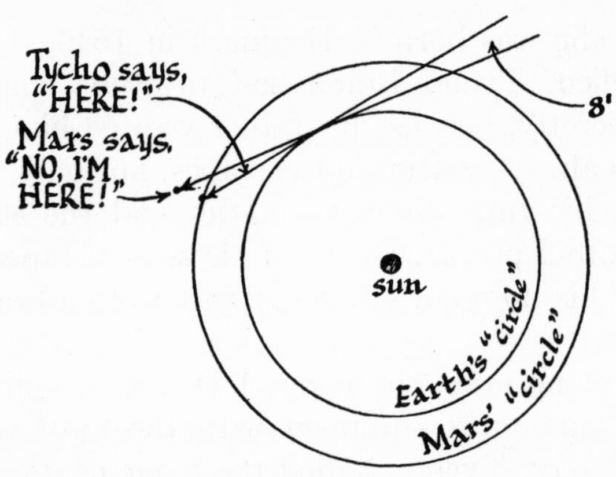

Of course Tycho was on the earth and it was moving around the sun "in a circle" and so was Mars. From his grave, Tycho told John to look for Mars along a certain line on a certain evening. John looked; but Mars wasn't there. Mars was 8′ (eight minutes) late. The angle between the line on which John looked and the line on which Mars actually was measured 8′. But 8′ in astronomy is terrifically large. John Kepler went to work with those 8′ to *reconstruct* the universe. Furthermore, he did!

"Circle . . . circle . . . circle . . .," John kept saying to himself. "Copernicus, yes even Plato, says that it should be a circle. But Mars does *not* move in a circle. It is 8′ out of line."

"Believe me, or believe what you see?" Copernicus taunted him from his grave.

"You and Plato, and Aristotle too for that matter, can go and jump in the lake," John replied. "My friend was a careful worker; and I believe my old friend, Tycho."

It is hard to tell why John Kepler thought of an ellipse at that moment. After all, why did Galileo gaze heavenward that day in the cathedral? Anyway, John Kepler thought of an ellipse; and that is what brings us back to the checkerboard.

Let's assume, just as an illustration, that Kepler had done all of his computations with a circle for Mars whose radius was 141,000,000 miles. That is about the average distance from the sun to Mars. The earth on the average is about 93,000,000 miles from the sun. You see where we get the expression, "astronomical figures." Well, so that we don't use up all of our scratchpaper writing down zeros, let's just talk about 141 million miles. The equation for Kepler's circle for Mars would be: $x^2 + y^2 = (141)^2$ or $x^2 + y^2 = 19{,}881{,}000{,}000{,}000{,}000$ miles, if we put in all the zeros.

Now suppose that we had studied Tycho Brahe's notebooks as John Kepler did. We couldn't get Mars to appear in the heavens where we computed it should be, moving around that circle.

So we decided to do as Kepler did. We tried an ellipse instead of that circle. The equation for the ellipse would be something like this:

$$\frac{x^2}{(1.5)^2} + \frac{y^2}{(1.3)^2} = 1$$

When y is 0, x is $\pm$ 1.5 (150,000,000 miles.)
When x is 0, y is $\pm$ 1.3 (130,000,000 miles.)

Let's put that ellipse on the plotting board, and use a dotted line to show the circle which we have discarded.

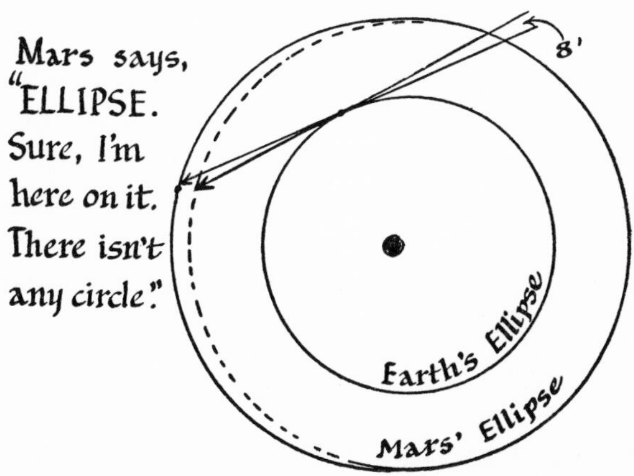

On the ellipse, Mars was where it belonged. The troublesome 8′ had disappeared. Tycho Brahe's notebooks were sound, after all. John Kepler's confidence in his old friend was justified. And that's the story on René Descartes' checkerboard in which John Kepler started with 8′ to reconstruct the universe. It remained for Sir Isaac Newton, one of the two inventors of calculus, to *explain why* Mars and the other planets move around the sun on paths, not circular, but elliptical.

Flying Off On a Calculated Tangent

DIFFERENTIAL CALCULUS

We've all used the expression, "Oh, he (or she) just flies off *on a tangent* every time you mention this (or that.)"

Maybe the family has been sitting around the dinner table and talking about things in general. Grandmother happens to mention that she has just received a letter from an old friend in France. That reminds Uncle John of his stamp collection; and off he flies *on a tangent* and talks for the next fifteen minutes about his stamp collection.

When men discovered calculus, they opened up a new department in the Department Store of Learning. This invention was another change which really separated the old-fashioned world from the modern world.

You remember that Galileo found out that a stone dropped 16 feet while his pendulum ticked off 1 second; fell 64 feet while the pendulum ticked off 2 seconds; fell 144 feet when 3 seconds had passed. The stone was speeding up with every passing second. Then Galileo found himself on the roof of The Leaning Tower of Pisa and had to stop his experiment. But he had discovered the Law of Falling Bodies, which in shorthand reads: "$d = 16t^2$." In other words, the distance that an object falls in any given number of seconds is 16 feet multiplied by the square of the number of seconds. In 1 second, the distance fallen is $16 \times 1 \times 1$ or 16 feet; in 2 seconds it is $16 \times 2 \times 2$ or 64 feet; in 3 seconds it is $16 \times 3 \times 3$ or 144 feet; and so on. If we put the story on Descartes' checkerboard, it makes part of a parabola.

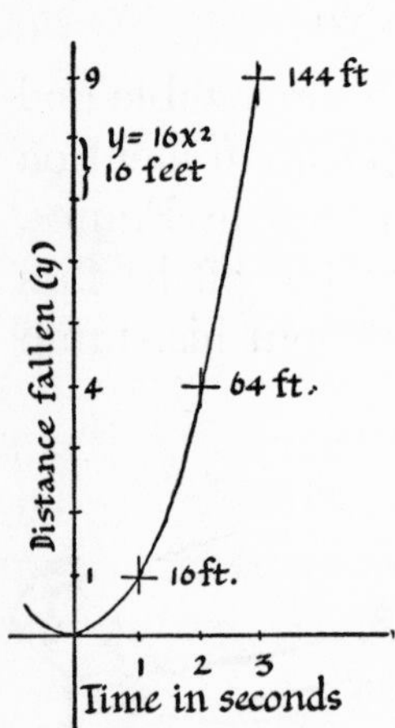

On the left is the graph which tells the story in the mathematical language of Descartes. It covers only the first 3 seconds.

On the right, however, is a moving picture of what happens during the first 10 seconds of a stone's fall. At the top is a huge cliff. It is night. Our helper has made a heavy little box containing a flashlight and an alarm clock. Every second the light flashes. It is a sort of falling lighthouse.

As our imaginary falling lighthouse drops, it gathers speed. You can tell that because, in the picture we see, the flashes are farther and farther apart. With the passing of every second, the flashes are more and more separated. Although the canyon is over 1,600 feet deep, our lighthouse finally bumps and is smashed into bits; but in the meantime our curiosity has been aroused.

How fast was it going at the end of the first second? How fast was it going at the end of the second, third, or fourth second? For that matter, how fast was it going at the end of any number of seconds? In other words, if the box also had contained a speedometer, what would the speedometer read at any given second? From zero when it was dropped at the top of the cliff, the speedometer would get faster, and *f a s t e r*, and F A S T E R until finally the flashing lighthouse bumped, registering the same sensation we have during a nightmare which horrifies us after eating too much mince pie late at night.

The Greeks and the Arabs had no tools in their mathematical workshops to solve a problem like this one. Most of their work was done with things which stood still or moved at a slow and fairly uniform speed. The modern world works with things which move. They move at very high speeds. They move at changing speeds, like the increasing speed of the falling lighthouse. Workers in the modern world simply had to invent new mathematical tools to work with on the new problems which came up.

Strangely enough, some of the new gadgets worked on with the new mathematics were destructive things like cannon balls, because cannons and hand guns were being used in war for the first time. Other things were useful in peacetime, like pumps and steam engines used in coal mines and factories. Anyway, without the new calculus, we probably would have had to wait a very long time for railroads and steamboats, automobiles and aeroplanes, radios and television sets.

So-o-o-o how fast was our falling lighthouse going at the end of the first second, the fifth, or the tenth? We can find out, if we can make it fly off Descartes' parabola *on a tangent.*

To see a little better what that means, let's look at this odd contraption. It is a whirling turntable, like the top of a phonograph. Glued to the whirling disc is a stick with three notches in it, 1 inch, 4 inches, and 9 inches from the center. In each notch is a ball-bearing about $\frac{1}{2}$ inch in diameter. As the disc whirls around, the ball-bearings stay in their notches. You can make it whirl fast or slow.

It also has a "wrecker." When you slide a stick in front of that little post at the side, the whirling stick stops dead. Of course the ball-bearings go shooting off *on a tangent.* All three of the ball-bearings shoot out of their notches. How far will each one go in one second? That is, what is the velocity of each one?

Well, if we had arranged a high-speed camera to take a picture exactly one second after the ball-bearings were jolted out of their notches and sent shooting off on their tangents, here is what the film would show:

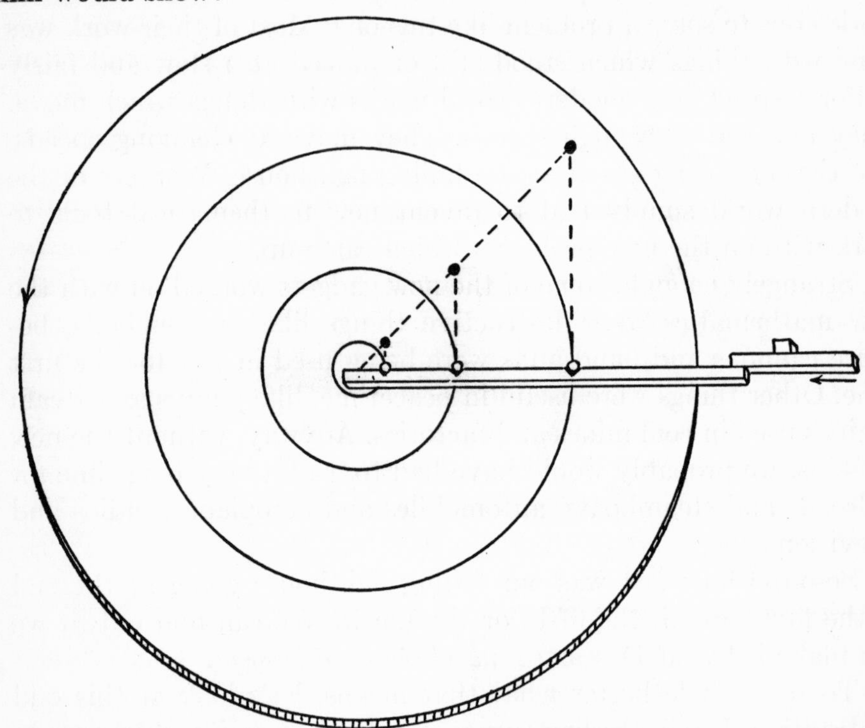

Each ball-bearing was going a certain distance in a circular path during the second just before the collision. During the next second when they shoot off on their tangents, they go just about those same distances. Had the turntable been whirling faster, each ball-bearing would have shot out farther. In other words, the distance each shoots out on its tangent during one second measures its velocity.

Now we come to *differential calculus* on the checkerboard.

The curve of the parabola on the graph gives us the picture of something falling faster and faster with the passing of every second. As a matter of fact, you square the number of seconds and multiply the result by 16 feet to find out how far (y distance) it had gone in x seconds. The equation for the parabola is: $y = 16x^2$.

Imagine that the curve of the parabola is a groove with a ball-bearing in it at the origin, that is at the point where y is zero and x is zero. Underneath the graph is a series of strong electric magnets. After 1 second, the magnets have pulled the ball-bearing to the point where y is 1 and x is 1. The ball-bearing started slowly and picked up speed so that at the end of 1 second it had reached 16 feet on the y line.

After 2 seconds, the magnets pulled the ball-bearing to the point where y is 4 and x is 2. ($y = x^2$.) It had reached 64 feet on the y line and still was gathering speed. After 3 seconds it was going still faster and had reached 144 feet on y. With each passing second, it was going faster and faster.

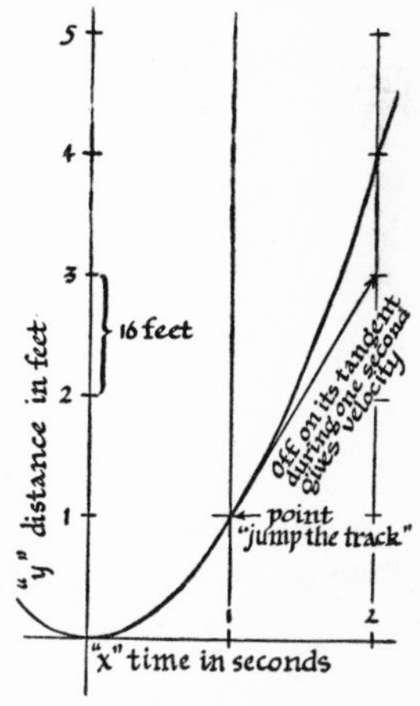

Now let's suppose that at any given instant, we can make the ball-bearing *jump the track!* It goes shooting off on its tangent. The electric magnets are turned off so that there is no more speeding up. If we had been taking high-speed moving pictures, the film exposed exactly 1 second after the ball-bearing jumped the track and scooted off on its tangent would tell us the velocity because it would show us the distance covered in 1 second. So if we can draw the tangent to the parabola at any given second and measure what distance on the y line that tangent covers before reaching the next x second line, we can also find out the velocity at that point. That is one of the types of problems solved by differential calculus.

All the points on the parabola meet the requirement that $y = x^2$. What requirements must be met by the line representing the tangent to the parabola at any given point? Well, it must touch the parabola at one point and at *only one* point. That is what a tangent to a parabola is. It is a straight line which touches the curve at only one point. It is rather hard to draw with a ruler and the naked eye; but by calculus it is easy and sure.

Rather stupidly, it seems, we start with a line which touches the curve at *two* points. It can't possibly be the tangent we are looking for; but it will lead us to it. Let's say that we are looking for the tangent to the parabola when the ball-bearing has been rolling along the magic groove for 1 second. At the point where x seconds is 1 and y distance is 1, ($y = x^2$), we want the ball-bearing to jump the track and shoot off for 1 second on the tangent to the curve at that point.

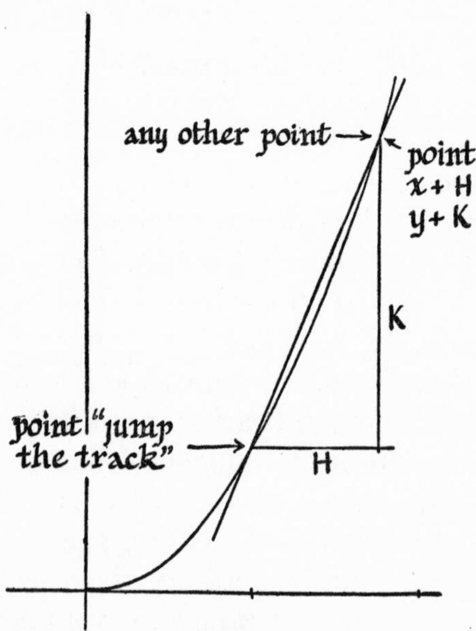

Quite intentionally, we pick out any other nearby point on the curve. We connect it with the point, "jump-the-track," by a straight line. We have a line we don't want. The problem now is to get the line we do want, one which touches the parabola, not at 2 points, but at only 1 point.

Both points are on our curve. At point "jump-the-track," x is 1 second and y is 1×1. The other point is $x + H$ seconds and $y + K$ distance from the first point. Since the second point is also on the curve on which all values of y must be the square of the corresponding x values, then $y + K$ must equal the square of $x + H$; that is $x + H$ times $x + H$.

We write out the equations for both points and subtract the equation for the first point from the second point's equation. That gives us a new equation about H and K which is also true.

From the equation for point 2,	$y + K = (x+H)^2 = x^2 + 2Hx + H^2$
Subtract the equation for point 1,	$y \qquad = x^2$
which gives:	$K = 2Hx + H^2$
which is the same as:	$K = H(2x + H)$
which is the same as:	$\frac{K}{H} = 2x + H$

That fraction $\frac{K}{H}$ is one in which we are *very definitely interested!* The plot involving the whole idea of calculus is about to thicken. $\frac{K}{H}$ is a fraction which measures the slope of a line which touches our curve at *two* points. The distance K is *a little bit of* y and the distance H is *a little bit of* x. Together K and H are two sides of a very important little triangle, the *Differential Triangle*. We have seen in the last equation above that when *a little bit of* K is divided by *a little bit of* H we get the fraction $\frac{K}{H}$ whose value is $2x + H$. That value is also the value of *Tangent* a, the angle made with the x ruler on the checkerboard by the line which touches our curve at 2 points.

Let's be *very sure* that we see *the point of the plot so far*. We

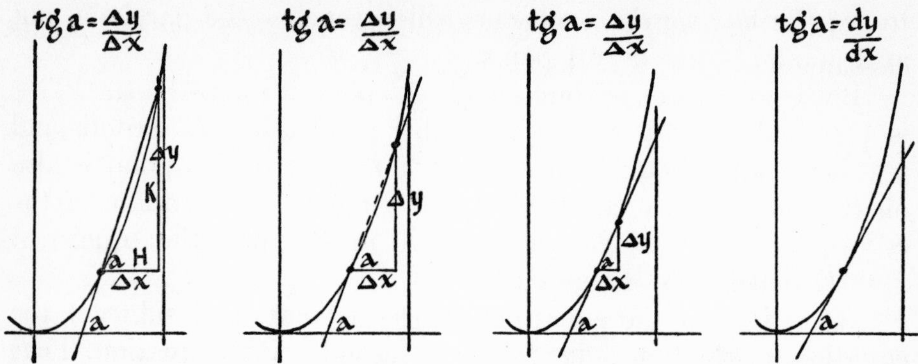

have a line which we do not want. It touches the parabola at 2 points. We want a line which touches the parabola at only 1 point. But the slope of that 2 point line which we do not want is $\frac{K}{H}$ and that is $2x + H$.

Now hold your breath for the final complication. The whole plot is about to unfold.

Pretend that the parabola is a thin steel wire. Pretend that it has two beads on it. The line which we do not want connects the two beads.

Move the top bead down the wire. Both K and H get shorter and shorter as you can see in the four diagrams above. The little diagram at the right shows the top bead moving down the wire. Do you see how the angle a changes every time the beads come closer to each other?

Nearer and nearer the top bead comes to the lower bead which is still at point, "jump-the-track." The angle a keeps changing ever so slightly.

Finally . . . *c l i c k!* Let's imagine that some magic has taken place. The two beads just snapped together and became one. Yes, *one single bead!* And our line now touches the curve at only one single point. *It is the line we want!* It is the line tangent to the parabola because it touches the curve at only 1 single point. And we know that the slope of that tangent line is $2x$.

"But," you will say, "when it touched the parabola at 2 points its slope was $2x + H$. What happened to H?"

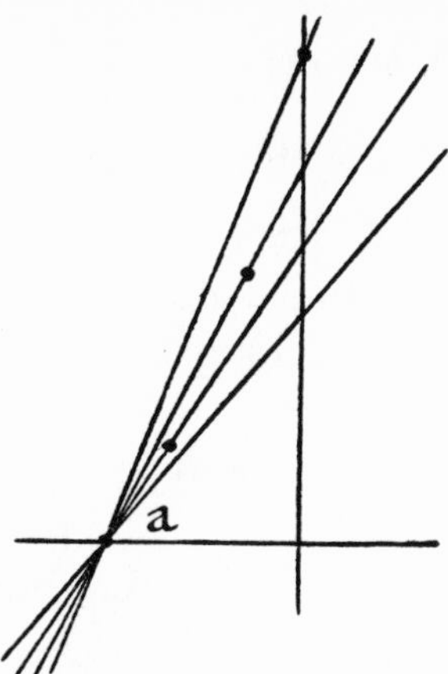

The answer to that question is, "H just got smaller and smaller and when the beads clicked not only H but also K just disappeared. They became too small to measure. They just *evaporated!*"

That is the secret of the whole plot of differential calculus. You start with a line which touches a curve at 2 points and know the slope which it makes with the x ruler. The slope is *a little bit of y* divided by *a little bit of x*, or as we called it $\frac{K}{H}$. Then you just boil down both H and K and they get smaller and smaller. You keep on boiling until finally they evaporate. At that point the two beads "click." What you have left is the slope of a line which touches the curve at 1 single point, and that is the tangent you were looking for. The slope of any tangent to the parabola, $y = x^2$, is $2x$. $\left(\text{Same as } \frac{2x}{1}\right)$.

Herr Professor Frederich Wilhelm Leibniz got tired of talking about *a little bit of y and x*. He called *a little bit of y* "Delta *y*." He called *a little bit of x* "Delta *x*." His native German language wasn't good enough for him so he invented some meaningless Greek jargon. That is, the Greeks wouldn't have known what he was talking about. The fraction $\frac{K}{H}$ in Leibniz' jargon looks like this: $\frac{\Delta y}{\Delta x}\cdot$ That is the fraction until the beads click. Then the fraction becomes $\frac{dy}{dx}\cdot$ That in differential calculus is known as the *differential coefficient* of y in respect to x. It is quite a mouthful. But all it means is the slope of the tangent to a curve.

My, but we have been a long time finding out how fast our ball-bearing was going at the end of the first second. We wanted to make it "jump the track" and shoot off on a tangent for 1 second in order to find its velocity. The trouble has come about in finding the tangent. But once we have found the tangent, everything will go on swimmingly from there.

How fast was the ball-bearing going when x was 1 second? It shot out of the groove on the tangent angle a whose slope is $\frac{dy}{dx}$ which is $\frac{2x}{1}\cdot$ In 1 second along this tangent it went from 16 feet on the y line to 48 feet. This is 32 feet. So its velocity *at the end of 1 second* was 32 feet per second.

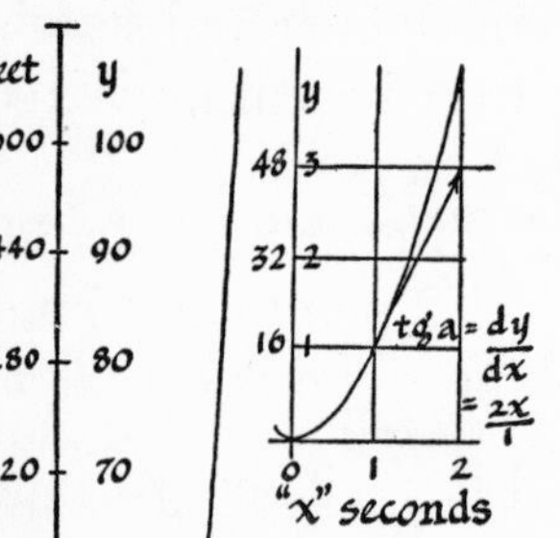

If our imaginary falling lighthouse were equipped with a speedometer, at the end of 1 second it would read 32 feet per second.

But what would the speedometer read after falling 10 seconds? After *any* number of seconds? All we need is the value of $\frac{dy}{dx}$, which is $\frac{2x}{1}\cdot$ When x is 10 seconds, $\frac{dy}{dx}$ is 20. So the speedometer would read 20 times 16 feet or 320 feet per second.

That 320 feet per second happens to be a little matter of 218 *miles per hour!* That's what the speedometer would read in our imaginary falling lighthouse 10 seconds after it fell off the top of the cliff.

When you stop to think about how many people wear out their tires and ruin the clutches in their automobiles when they try to speed up from 0 to 25 or 30 miles an hour in 10 seconds, you are impressed by the strength of this strange new force, gravity, which men started to study in the days of Galileo. No wonder Galileo wished that The Leaning Tower of Pisa were higher. Leibniz made it possible to build on paper a Leaning Tower as high as desired. But we should remember that, in an automobile going only 60 miles an hour, "the wind" or air resistance is so strong that you can hardly open a door. A stone dropping through the air would be braked down to something considerably less than 218 miles per hour in a 10 second fall. But in a vacuum, it would fall that fast. And strangely enough, so would a feather!

Phew!

It's time for a breather. It's time for a few moments of puffing.

It's time for a breather. It's time for a few moments for puffing. If you do not understand all the details of differential calculus on the first trip through this chapter don't get discouraged; a second trip through it may convince you that you understood a fair amount on the first trip. Most people learn calculus by the "plodding" method. Very few really "romp."

So if Uncle John flying off from the family dinner table on a tangent, and the clockwork-flashlight falling off a cliff, and the ball-bearing shooting out of the magic groove all leave you a little groggy, keep up your courage. Have heart; for you are now frequenting the company not only of Leibniz but also of the immortal Newton. And Newton is the man who solved the riddle of what makes the universe hang together.

The Ticking Hair Clipper

INTEGRAL CALCULUS

THIS is a very special type of hair clipper because it has a taxicab meter on it. It is a purely imaginary instrument and can have no practical use in real life, except to help in explaining what integral calculus is. Calculus by itself means a little counting stone, or a pebble. Integral calculus uses the kind of counting stones which enable you to add up the number of squares there are in the surface of an area which would be exceedingly difficult to measure, in fact impossible without calculus.

Almost any area bounded by a curved line is very hard to measure. If you want to find how many square inches there are in a table top, all you do is measure the length, which turns out to be three feet, and the width, which turns out to be two feet, and multiply the two dimensions to get six square feet as the area. In geometry and in trigonometry, tools were found to measure any surface bounded by straight lines. You just break up the area into a number of triangles, and then multiply the base of each triangle by half it's height.

However, here are some problems. How are you going to find length and width so that you can multiply the two?

The shaded areas are what we want to measure. And there just are *no lengths* and *widths* to multiply together to get their areas!

The first figure is bounded by the x horizontal ruler and the y vertical ruler on the Descartes checkerboard and by a curved line which we recognize as part of the circumference of a circle. Our eye tells us that it looks like part of a circle and the formula, $x^2 + y^2 = 16$, tells us that it *is* a circle.

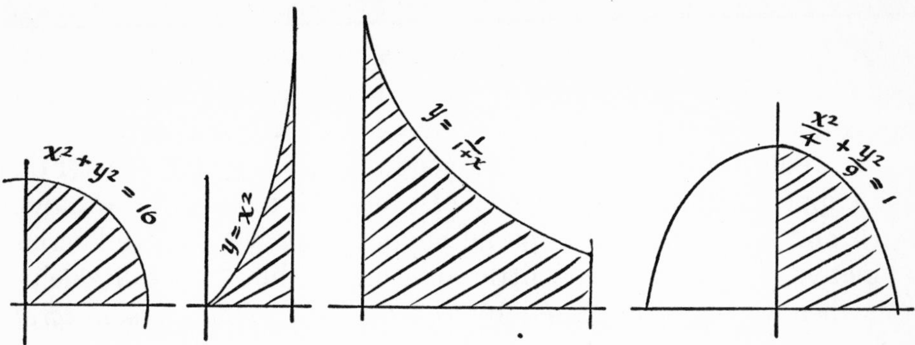

The second figure is our frequently encountered friend, the parabola, whose y value increases by leaps and bounds, 0 to 1 to 4 to 9 to 16 and so on while its x value goes plodding along, 0 to 1 to 2 to 3 to 4 and so on. In the mathematical language of Descartes, this parabola is built according to the plan, $y = x^2$.

The third figure is a new acquaintance, an hyperbola, $y = \frac{1}{1+x}$. You can see that when x is put into the formula as zero, y equals one over one or 1. But when x is 1, y is $\frac{1}{2}$; when x is 2, y is $\frac{1}{3}$; when x is 3, y is $\frac{1}{4}$; when x is 1,000, y is $\frac{1}{1{,}001}$; and when x is 1,000,000, y is $\frac{1}{1{,}000{,}001}$. In other words, that right wing of the hyperbola is a very annoying thing and a very peculiar kind of curve. However long we make x, the y gets closer and closer to the x ruler but *never* quite meets it.

The fourth figure is an old friend, an ellipse, a sort of steel barrel hoop that started as a circle but got squeezed in between two boxes. It is planned according to the formula for an ellipse with a major axis of 3 and a minor axis of 2 as follows: $\frac{x^2}{4} + \frac{y^2}{9} = 1$.

But we have been an extraordinarily long time looking over the odd shapes of the customers to be clipped and have neglected the very special type of clipper with which we are going to do the job. About all we are convinced of is that measuring the areas of these odd shaped pieces is a new and tough job, without calculus.

We had better take a look at the hair clipper with taximeter attached. Of course the cutting edge is a series of sharp teeth which move back and forth above a toothed guide. Every time a hair gets in between the teeth, it is snipped off as the teeth move.

It would be easy enough for a good mechanic to put a meter on the clipper to count the number of times the teeth were to move back and forth. Our very special clipper has a very special series of meters, purely imaginary little counting machines but quite helpful when we are confronted by the question, *How does integral calculus work?*

Every single tooth is connected up with its own meter. As long as a single hair is clipped, the meter for that particular tooth clicks. When there is no hair to be clipped, the meter stops. Then there is a master meter which gives the sum total of the count on all the tiny individual meters.

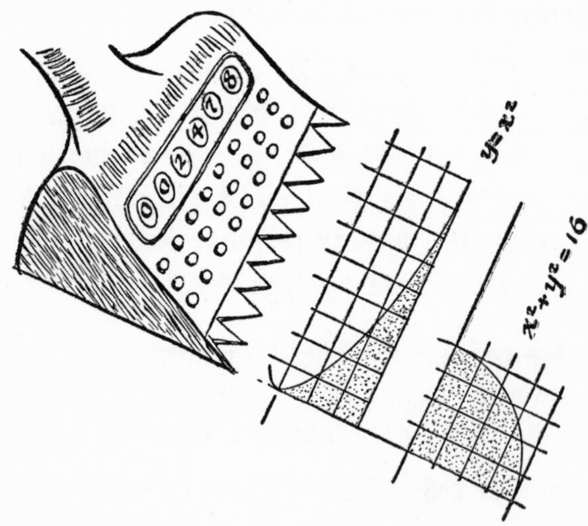

Quite a gadget, isn't it? Here it is all set to "clip off" the answers to two problems: the area bounded by the parabola, $y = x^2$, up to the limiting line, $x = 3$; and $\frac{1}{4}$ the area of circle, $x^2 + y^2 = 16$.

Buzzzzzzzzzz. Whirrrrrrr. It's turned on and ready to work. Of course the meter is set at zero on the master meter and on all the little single meters for the individual teeth. Slowly it moves forward along the x ruler. The teeth actually are $\frac{1}{5}$ of an inch apart and every time they move the clipper moves forward $\frac{1}{5}$ of an inch.

At first the teeth on the right start to clip behind the line, $y = x^2$. When the first row of squares is passed, more teeth clip off the imaginary hair. More and more of the little single tooth meters start clicking. The master meter starts clicking faster and faster. In the third row of squares, practically all the little meters are clicking and the master meter is having a hard time to keep up with its job, it is clicking so fast.

The meter registers 322 twenty-fifths of a square inch, or 12.88 square inches, for the quarter-circle, $x^2+y^2=16$. (This is an error of about 2.5% over.)

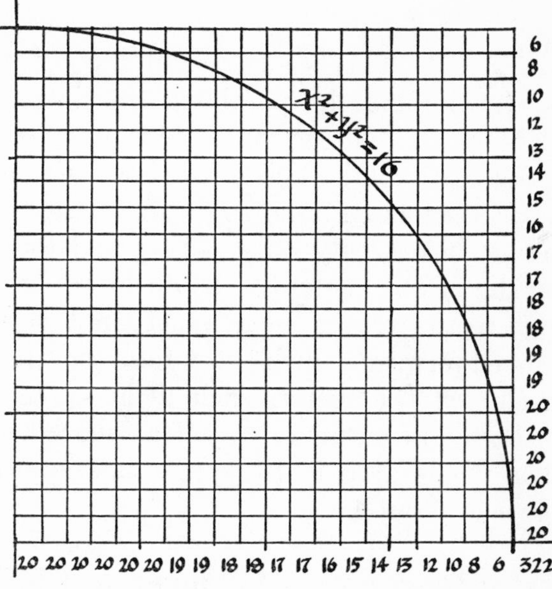

Then, suddenly, as the third line is passed, the clicking stops. Nothing more is registering on the single meters and the master meter stands still, too. We take a reading on the master meter, make a note of it, and set it back to zero.

On we go with the integral calculus clipper to the quarter-circle. There the first twenty teeth plunge into the job all together but none of the other teeth has anything to do. One by one the teeth on the left run out of work and stop clicking their meters. Finally the boundary of the circle is passed and all the teeth have stopped clicking and so have their meters. We make a note of the reading on the master meter.

Here is a picture of what has happened.

The meter registers 322 twenty-fifths of a square inch, or 12.88 square inches, for the quarter-circle, $x^2 + y^2 = 16$. (This is an error of about 2.5% over.)

The meter registers 250 twenty-fifths of a square inch, or 10 square inches, as the area bounded by the parabola, $y = x^2$, between the lines where $x = 3$ and $x = 0$. (This is an error of about 10% over.)

In clipping the parabola, the first tooth on the right of the clipper clicked 15 times on its meter, the second tooth clicked 13 times, the next two 12 each, then 11 . . . and so on up to the top where six teeth clicked only once. The grand total, however, on the master meter was 250 little squares. Since the teeth were $\frac{1}{5}$ inch apart, and since they moved forward $\frac{1}{5}$ inch every time they registered a clip on the meter, each little square is $\frac{1}{5}$ times $\frac{1}{5}$ of an inch or $\frac{1}{25}$ of a square inch. The whole area is 10 square inches. The error is about 10%.

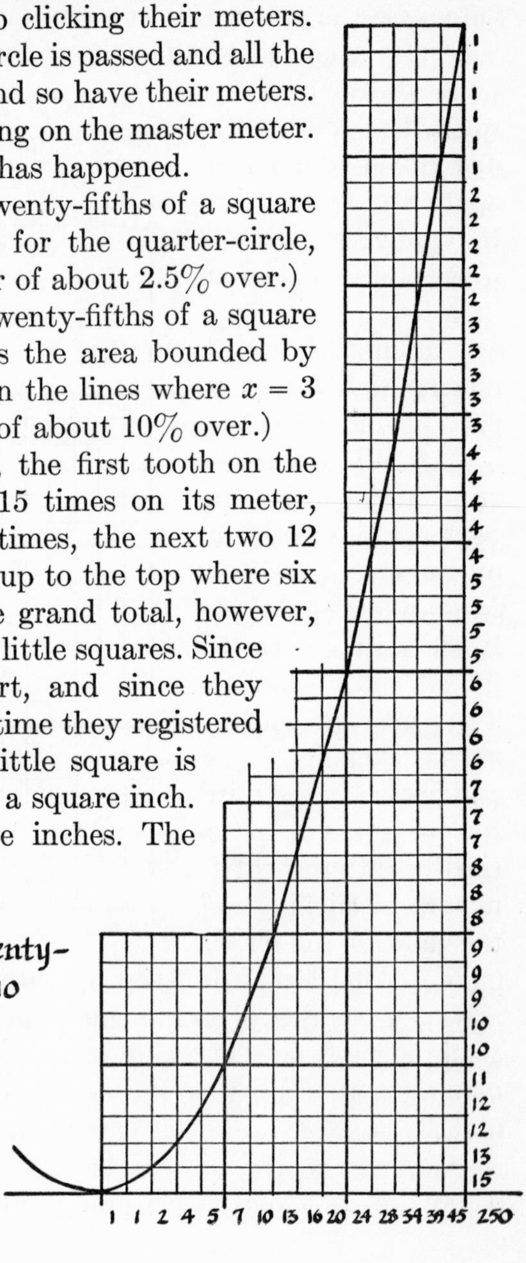

The meter registers 250 twenty-fifths of a square inch, or 10 square inches, as the area bounded by the parabola, $y = x^2$, between the lines where $x = 3$ and $x = 0$. (This is an error of about 10% over.)

In clipping the quarter-circle, the first 20 teeth went into action right away. One by one the teeth on the left stopped clipping and therefore stopped clicking. When the entire job was finished, the meter registered the grand total of 322 little squares, or $\frac{322}{25}$ square inches which is 12.88 square inches. Since almost everyone knows that the area of a circle is π times the square of the radius, in this case $4 \times 4 \times 3.14159$ or 50.265 square inches for the whole circle and 12.57 square inches for the quarter-circle, we can check up on the error of the Ticking Hair Clipper. The error is about 2.5%.

For the time being, we need not worry too much about either that 10% error or that 2.5% error, because there is a cure for it. In fact the method of curing it is the secret of integral calculus. Let's catch our breath for a moment, and have a look around the room at the company we're keeping. There is Sir Isaac Newton who lived in England (1642–1727) and Frederich Wilhelm Leibniz who lived in Germany (1646–1716). Both of them did many important things other than calculus. Although they never worked together, both are given credit for being the inventors of calculus. Way back in the corner is a modest little fellow, Professor Barrow. Newton went to his classes at Cambridge University. When the student Newton was only 27 years old, Professor Barrow resigned his professorship and gave it to Newton. What a brain in Newton! What a sport in Barrow! As a matter of fact, there might not have been any calculus for a long time without Barrow, for that little disappearing triangle which we saw in the differential calculus is called Barrow's Triangle, and he taught it to Newton.

Newton went on and on and on, into unknown fields. He applied his mathematics to all sorts of difficult problems in mechanics, in physics, in astronomy. In astronomy, he went to work on gravity where Galileo left off. He figured out the theory which says this force of gravity, which we feel when we jump off a chair, exists between any two objects such as the earth and the moon, the sun and the earth, the sun and all its other planets. How much it pulls depends on the size of the body and the distance it is from another body. For example, in a rocket going toward the moon, the first part of the journey would be spent in overcoming the pull back to earth but on the end of the trip, you'd have to bail out of the rocket and use a parachute because gravity on the moon would be pulling you. Well, Newton figured all that out. He was a good sport too. When he was an old man he said, "If I have seen farther than others it is because I have stood on the shoulders of giants." That's a rather kind compliment to all the mathematicians who had lived before him, not to mention Professor Barrow.

Now let's return to that 10% error and the ticking hair clipper. You remember that the teeth were $\frac{1}{5}$ of an inch apart and moved forward $\frac{1}{5}$ inch every time they clicked. That is how the little squares $\frac{1}{25}$ of a square inch were formed and counted.

Supposing the teeth were made finer, say $\frac{1}{10}$ of an inch, and the distance they advanced on each clip, $\frac{1}{10}$ of an inch. Do you see that, instead of having $\frac{1}{25}$th inch squares, we would now have $\frac{1}{100}$th inch squares? Or let's make the teeth 50 to the inch and the forward movement only $\frac{1}{50}$th of an inch. Then there would be 2,500 tiny squares in one square inch. The meters would have to do a great deal more counting, but the errors in measuring the area bounded by the curve would be growing smaller and smaller.

Without worrying too much about the construction of our ticking clipper, for after all it is only an imaginary ticking clipper, let's imagine a clipper with teeth too small to measure. The *error* would be *too small* to measure and so could be *ignored.*

On the next page is a convincing picture, showing the way to eliminate error by making the size of the counted squares smaller and smaller. The curve is the same $y = x^2$ curve. It has been placed under a strong magnifying glass and shows the square from x and y equal zero to x and y equal 1. It is the same one square inch which we saw when looking at the results of using 25 squares to the square inch.

The solid line to the left of the curve shows the error when 25 squares to the inch are used. It is an error of about 10%. The dotted line shows how a great deal of the error is eliminated when 100 squares to the inch are used. That cuts down the error to about 5%. The very fine saw tooth line shows how small the error becomes when the squares are $\frac{1}{200} \times \frac{1}{200}$ inch or $\frac{1}{40{,}000}$ of a square inch. Remember the total error was only 10% at first! Then it was brought down to 5%. If the ticking hair clipper had 200 very fine teeth to the inch, the error would be reduced to less than $\frac{1}{10}$th of 1%.

But that is not good enough for integral calculus. Frederich Wilhelm Leibniz wanted his results absolutely accurate. And he is the gentleman who taught us how to get the Integral Coefficient for a formula such as the one we are working with: $y = x^2$. The Integral Coefficient gives us mathematically the meter reading on the ticking hair clipper when the teeth are too fine to measure and therefore the error too fine to measure.

Here's what it is, as worked out once and for all by Leibniz:

Area bounded by the curve, $y = x^2$, when x is 3:

$$\frac{1}{2+1}\{3^3 - 0^3\}$$

This works out to be $\frac{1}{3}(27)$, making the area 9.

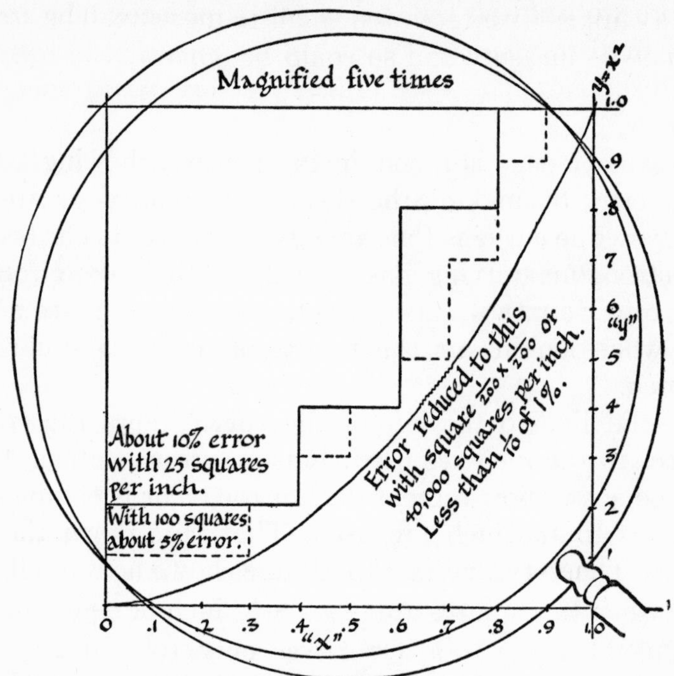

In other words, when our ticking hair clipper gave us an answer of 10 square inches with 5 teeth to the inch, it was off about 10%; when we doubled the number of teeth, it was off about 5%; when there were 200 teeth to the inch, the clipper was off about $\frac{1}{10}$ of 1% and should have read about 9.009 square inches. Still that was not good enough. With Leibniz' help, we find that it is exactly 9 square inches.

You haven't been told how to make Integral Coefficients. And you are not going to be told now. When you go to college will be soon enough. And in strictest secrecy, you may find that a great many people who use Integral Coefficients in real life and build huge bridges and plan enormous dams and design aeroplane engines don't work out their integrals for themselves. They read them in books, and use them as we have done with $y = x^2$ and are going to do again.

Before we come to the end of our trip, a-romping through the fields of mathematics, let's have an ice cream cone together. And let's find out how much ice cream the cone could hold, if it were filled up.

A cone is a very difficult thing to measure. The bottom part of it fills up so much faster than the top part which keeps on getting wider and wider. One really must have calculus to measure the cone accurately.

Our cone when 5 inches tall has a radius of 1 inch. The main thing which makes it so difficult to measure is that the radius keeps changing all the time. When the cone is only $2\frac{1}{2}$ inches tall, the radius is only $\frac{1}{2}$ inch. If the height of the cone were to increase to 10 inches, the radius would increase to 2 inches.

The cone's volume depends of course not only on its height but also on the square of its radius. In fact, to get the area of a circular slice of the cone at any height, you square the radius and multiply by 3.14159, that is πR^2. So we see that the volume of a cone grows as its height grows. We are going to call its height "x." It also grows very rapidly in volume as each succeeding circular slice increases in area. The increase depends on the *square* of the radius times π. Since, in our particular cone, the radius is always $\frac{1}{5}$ of the height, any circular slice of the cone will have an area of $\pi\left(\frac{x}{5}\right)^2$.

Let's watch our 5 inch cone grow up from a little 1 inch cone. When it is only 1 inch tall, its radius is $\frac{1}{5}$ of that or 0.2″. The area of its base, πR^2, is only about $\frac{1}{8}$ of a square inch. (0.2×0.2 equals 0.04. Then 3.14159×0.04 equals 0.1256636 or about $\frac{1}{8}$ square inch.)

A cone 1″ tall	has a radius 0.2″	and the area of its base is about $\frac{1}{8}$ sq. in.
2″	0.4″	$\frac{1}{2}$ sq. in.
3″	0.6″	1.13 sq. in.
4″	0.8″	2.01 sq. in.
5″	1.0″	3.14 sq. in.

At the left is a little cone 1″ tall. At a first glance, we can see that the next cone which is 2″ tall is large enough to hold several

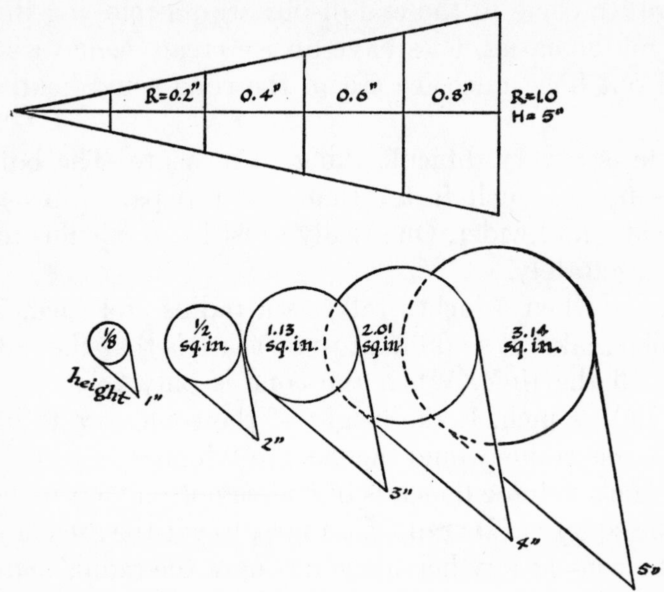

of the little 1″ cones. The 3″ cone probably would hold 20 or 25. The 4″ cone looks as though it would hold 50 or more and the 5″ cone probably twice that number. We are satisfied that we have a rather tough new problem of measuring on our hands!

For a few minutes, let's pretend that integral calculus hasn't been invented. We shall try to measure the volume of the 5″ cone by "the brute strength and awkwardness" method. To do this we shall make it into a series of cylinders: first one cylinder, then two, three, four, five, and finally ten cylinders. Each time we increase the number of cylinders, the accuracy of our answer improves; but what an enormous amount of work is involved!

The volume of each cylinder appears on its graph in shaded lines. Height in inches is shown along the x line. Along the y line is the area in square inches of the cylinder's base. When base is multiplied by height, the result is volume. So the shaded lines show the volume graphically.

For example, the volume of the first cylinder appears on the

Radius of Cylinder	R^2	πR^2
.5	.25	.7854
.25	.0625	.1963
.75	.5625	1.767
.1667	.0278	.087
.5000	.2500	.785
.8333	.6944	2.182
.125	.015625	.0491
.375	.140625	.4418
.625	.390625	1.2272
.875	.765625	2.4053
.1	.01	.031
.3	.09	.283
.5	.25	.785
.7	.49	1.539
.9	.81	2.545
.05	.0025	.0079
.15	.0225	.0707
.25	.0625	.1963
.35	.1225	.3848
.45	.2025	.6362
.55	.3025	.9503
.65	.4225	1.3273
.75	.5625	1.7671
.85	.7225	2.2698
.95	.9025	2.8353

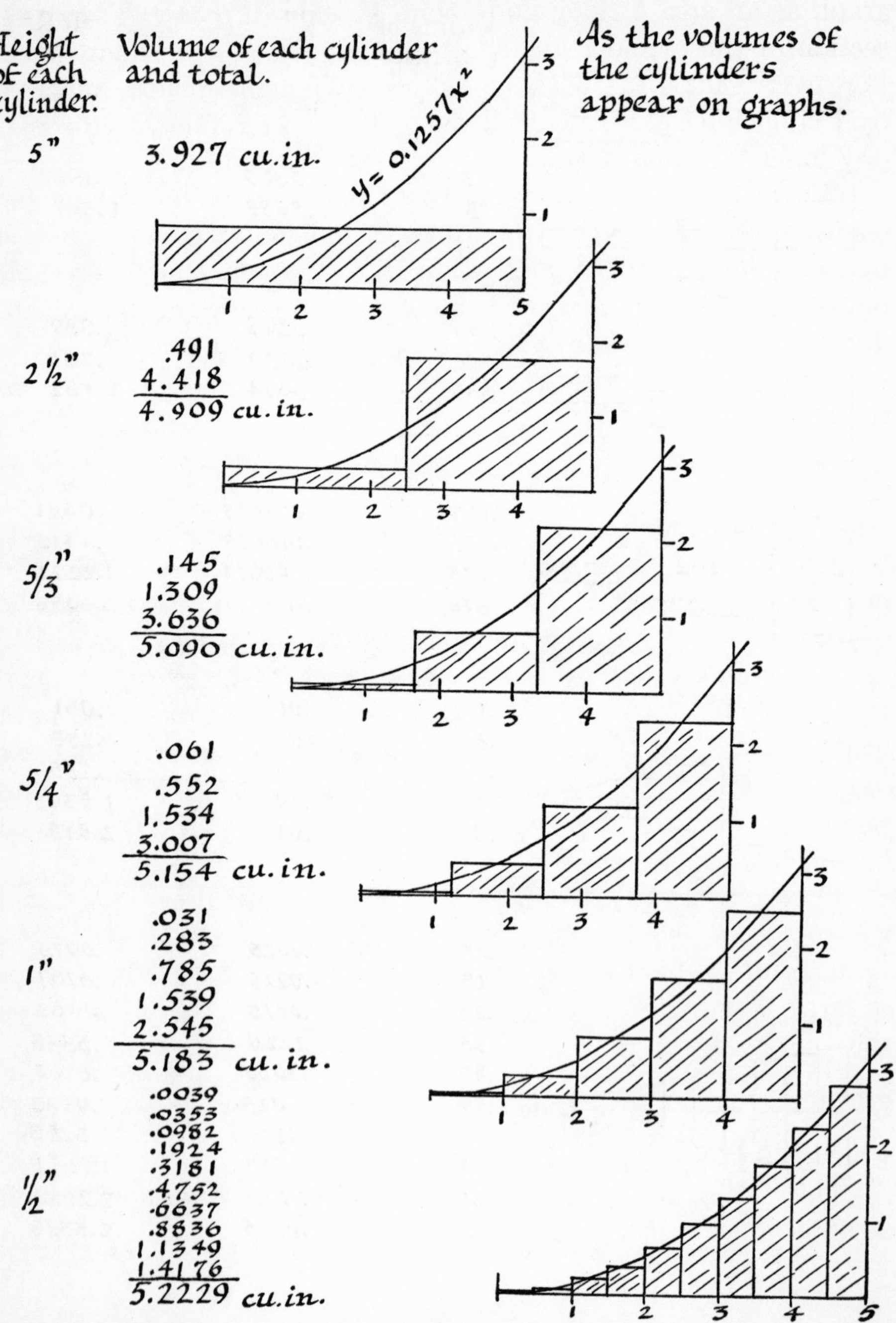
Height of each cylinder.
Volume of each cylinder and total.
As the volumes of the cylinders appear on graphs.
y = 0.1257x²
5"
3.927 cu.in.
2½"
.491
4.418
4.909 cu.in.
5/3"
.145
1.309
3.636
5.090 cu.in.
5/4"
.061
.552
1.534
3.007
5.154 cu.in.
1"
.031
.283
.785
1.539
2.545
5.183 cu.in.
½"
.0039
.0353
.0982
.1924
.3181
.4752
.6637
.8836
1.1349
1.4176
5.2229 cu.in.

graph as an area 5″ long and about $\frac{3}{4}$″ wide (0.7854″). The cross-section of the cylinder has an area of about $\frac{3}{4}$ of a square inch. For every added 1″ of height, the cylinder's volume increases by $\frac{3}{4}$ cubic inch. When the cylinder is 5″ tall, its volume is 5(0.7854) or 3.927 cubic inches.

When the cone is represented by two cylinders, the volume becomes 4.909 cubic inches; by three cylinders, 5.090 cubic inches; by four cylinders, 5.154 cubic inches; by five cylinders, 5.183 cubic inches; and finally when the cone is sliced up into ten small cylinders, its volume seems to be very close to 5.2229 cubic inches.

Perhaps you have started to wonder what that curved line on the graph is.

That curved line is the parabola, $y = \pi\left(\frac{x}{5}\right)^2$, or $0.1257x^2$. It tells how fast the cylinder's volume is growing as its height grows.

And do you see how our saw-toothed line comes nearer and nearer to marking off an area equal to that enclosed by the parabola, every time we increase the number of divisions along the x line?

As anyone can see, it has been quite a bit of work to compute the volume of ten slices of the cone. What an enormous amount of work it would be to compute the volume of 100 slices! But if we did, the *error* for the volume of the cone would get *smaller* and *smaller*. If we computed the volume of 1,000 slices, the *error* would be *still smaller*.

But we could go on and on until we were gray headed, and still we would not get the answer exactly right.

The integral calculus permits us to make the number of slices so large that the error just disappears. All we have to do is to use the "integral" of the formula which shows how fast our cone is growing. Our cone is growing at the rate of πR^2, that is $3.14159\left(\frac{x}{5}\right)^2$, which is $0.1257x^2$.

The "integral" for $1x^2$ or $2x^2$ or $0.1257x^2$, or any other x^2 such as ax^2 is:

$$\frac{a}{n+1}x^{(n+1)}.$$

So the "integral" for $0.1257x^2$ is $\dfrac{0.1257}{2+1}x^{(n+1)}$ or $0.04189x^3$. Since x is the height of the cone or 5″, the volume of our cone is $0.04189(5^3)$ or $0.04189(125)$ or 5.236 cubic inches.

Yes, that's all there is to it, once you discard the "brute strength and awkwardness" method and use integral calculus instead. It is a hard tool to understand; but once you know how to use it, the results are quick and sure.

Now that we have taken quite a long time to find out how much ice cream one cone holds, let's compute the volume of three or four more cones in the wink of an eye.

Our 5″ cone is replaced by a 10″ cone. All that is necessary is to replace the figure 5″ by the figure 10″:

$$0.04189(10^3) \text{ or } 0.04189(1{,}000) = 41.89 \text{ cubic inches.}$$

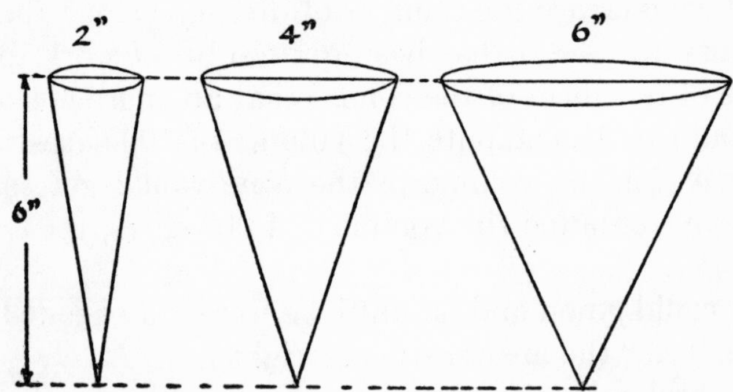

Let's examine the capacity of three different cones, each six inches tall. The first one has a radius $\frac{1}{6}$ its height, the second's radius is $\frac{1}{3}$ its height, and the third's radius is $\frac{1}{2}$ its height. They all grow as their heights increase according to πR^2:

$$\pi\left(\frac{x}{6}\right)^2; \quad \pi\left(\frac{x}{3}\right)^2; \quad \text{and} \quad \pi\left(\frac{x}{2}\right)^2; \quad \text{respectively.}$$

When we do the necessary arithmetic, we find that their rates of growth are:

$$\frac{\pi}{36}x^2 = .08726x^2; \quad \frac{\pi}{9}x^2 = .34906x^2; \quad \text{and} \quad \frac{\pi}{4}x^2 = .7854x^2.$$

To find the volume of each cone, all that remains is to use the "integral," $\frac{a}{n+1}x^{(n+1)}$, when x is 6″, the height of the cone:

$\frac{.08726}{2+1}(6^{[2+1]}) = .02909(216) = 6.28344$ cu. in. capacity of first cone.

$\frac{.34906}{2+1}(6^{[2+1]}) = .11635(216) = 25.1316$ cu. in. capacity of second cone.

$\frac{.7854}{2+1}(6^{[2+1]}) = .2618(216) = 56.5488$ cu. in. capacity of third cone.

That's how quickly and accurately problems are solved when you are able to use integral calculus. The method is certainly much better than "brute strength and awkwardness."

Remembering our ancient Egyptian friends and the Pyramid of Giza, isn't it a temptation to measure its volume in cubic yards of stone required to build it? The Egyptians were able to do it only by the "brute strength and awkwardness" method. We are able to use integral calculus.

The pyramid measures 9,068.8 inches at its base and is 5,776 inches high. These dimensions in yards are 251.9 yards at the base and 160.4 yards high. We shall use round numbers in our calculus problem: base 250 yards, height 160 yards.

If you care to spend a long, tedious, and rainy afternoon using arithmetic, try to figure out the volume of the pyramid. You might start with the bottom layer of stones, 250 yards by 250 yards, which will give you 62,500 cubic yards, if your blocks are 1 yard in height. Then set the next layer back just far enough to make the slope correct and put on the next layer. Don't forget the odd shaped stones for the edges and the corners. It will be a tedious

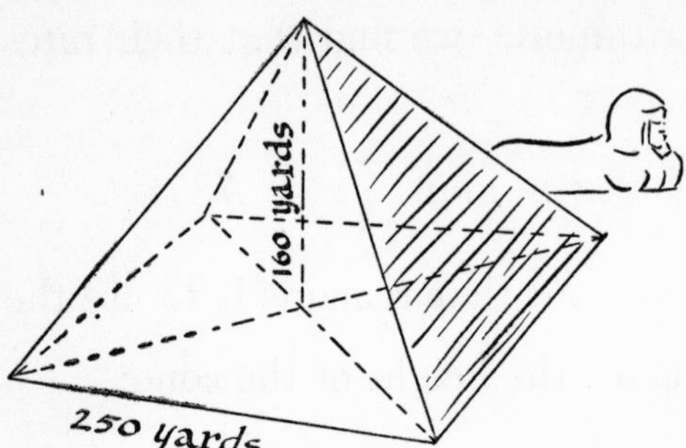

afternoon, indeed. It will improve your gratitude for the integral calculus.

Well, in calculus, the first thing we must find out is ratio of the base to the height.

$$\frac{\text{250 yards in the base}}{\text{160 yards of height}} = 1.56\tfrac{1}{4}.$$

So at any given height of the pyramid, the area of the square base increases at the rate of $(1.56\frac{1}{4})(1.56\frac{1}{4})$ or more than 2.44 times the rate the height increases. As the height (which we call x) grows, the volume grows at the rate of $2.44140625x^2$. Let's apply the "integer" when x is 160 yards. (You will soon see why we carried that decimal out to 8 places for 1.5625^2!!!)

Well, the "integer" is $\dfrac{a}{n+1}x^{(n+1)}$ or $\dfrac{a}{3}x^3$.

Inserting the values of a and x, we have: $\dfrac{2.44140625}{3}(160^3)$.

This is $2.44140625 \times 4{,}096{,}000 \div 3$ or $3{,}333{,}333\frac{1}{3}$ cubic yards of stone. That is exactly *one-third* of *ten million cubic yards* of stone!

That exact third of ten million gives us something to ponder. Have we hit upon one of the mysteries of the Pyramid of Giza? Is this one of the mathematical secrets of the Sphinx?

Of course the ancient Egyptians didn't have the modern English and American yard for measuring; but they did have the length of a man's stride. It looks as though that unit of measuring has changed very little in these thousands of years.

Nor did the Egyptians have the modern calculus which we have used to measure the Pyramid's volume. They did have fractions, however, and they seem to have worked wonders with them.

Let's assume that the Egyptians knew that the volume of a pyramid was $\frac{1}{3}$ the volume of the cube which would contain it. They could easily have found that out by slicing a cube of wet clay and then weighing both the pyramid and the chunks left over. And let's assume that Egyptian builders used 400 paces as a convenient distance unit, just as we use it for a 400 yard dash.

The Pyramid of Giza is very, very nearly 250 yards square at the base and 160 yards high. Well, here are some interesting fractions:

$$\frac{250}{400} = \frac{5}{8} \qquad \frac{160}{400} = \frac{2}{5}$$

The cube which would contain the pyramid would be

$$\frac{5}{8} \times \frac{5}{8} \times \frac{2}{5} = \frac{50}{320}\text{; and } \frac{1}{3} \text{ of that would be } \frac{50}{960}.$$

So the pyramid would be $\frac{50}{960}$ of a cube $400 \times 400 \times 400$ Egyptian paces or $\frac{5}{96}$ of 64,000,000. . .

Is that a smile or a smirk on the face of the Sphinx as we are about to . . .

$$\frac{5}{96} \text{ of } 64{,}000{,}000 \text{ equals } \ldots\ 3{,}333{,}333\tfrac{1}{3}!!!$$

Maybe this is ALL the arithmetic which the Egyptian architect did: $400 \times 400 \times 400 \times \frac{5}{8} \times \frac{5}{8} \times \frac{2}{5} \times \frac{1}{3} = 3{,}333{,}333\frac{1}{3}$ to get the number of cubic yards of stone required to build the Pyramid of Giza.

On one point there is no mystery. If each of 10,000 men each year quarried, cut, transported, and put in place 10 stones 1 cubic yard in size, it would take them 33 years and 4 months to complete the tomb of the Egyptian King in the Pyramid of Giza. That gives us some idea of what an enormous task it was.

With all of our pondering and our marvelling, we've almost forgotten about the little ice cream cone which we were going to have before parting. It is the first one we measured, the one which holds $5\frac{1}{4}$ cubic inches of ice cream. That is $5\frac{1}{4}$ cubic inches, unless it's heaped up on top.

At this point in our long romping journey through mathematics, we certainly are going to have it heaped up high on top! Then we shall propose a toast to Sir Isaac Newton and Herr Frederich Wilhelm Leibniz.

The Rompers' Timetable

REVIEW

When time comes for reviewing any part of mathematics, it's generally a headache for the student. There are all the facts between the green or blue or brown covers of that impersonal book. Whatever the color, at this time it generally looks blue!

We feel that we are very slow and possibly somewhat stupid students to take such a long time to learn what's between the covers of that book. No one tells us what a long time, how many centuries and centuries, it took our ancestors and their friends in all parts of the world to collect and arrange the mental tools for counting and measuring.

For us Rompers, reviewing is going to be different this time. Most of the work is going to be done by the artist. In the picture we are going to be standing somewhere in that wonderland of the year Anno Domini 1999, or perhaps it is 2001. We are looking back at the path along which we have romped.

It is a wide path at first, in fact it stretches all around the earth. It is filled with aeroplanes, ocean liners, fast automobiles . . . all of them speeding into the future. Radio . . . the atomic bomb.

Near the 1900 line, there is the high-slung gasoline buggy, the electric light, and one of the Wright Brothers in that haywire flying machine. The railroad made its way across the world during the 19th century. That's the time the first little paddlewheel steamship ventured out on the broad oceans.

Back of the 1800 line is Napoleon's artillery on Descartes' checkerboard and James Watt's steam engine which started so much going in the following century.

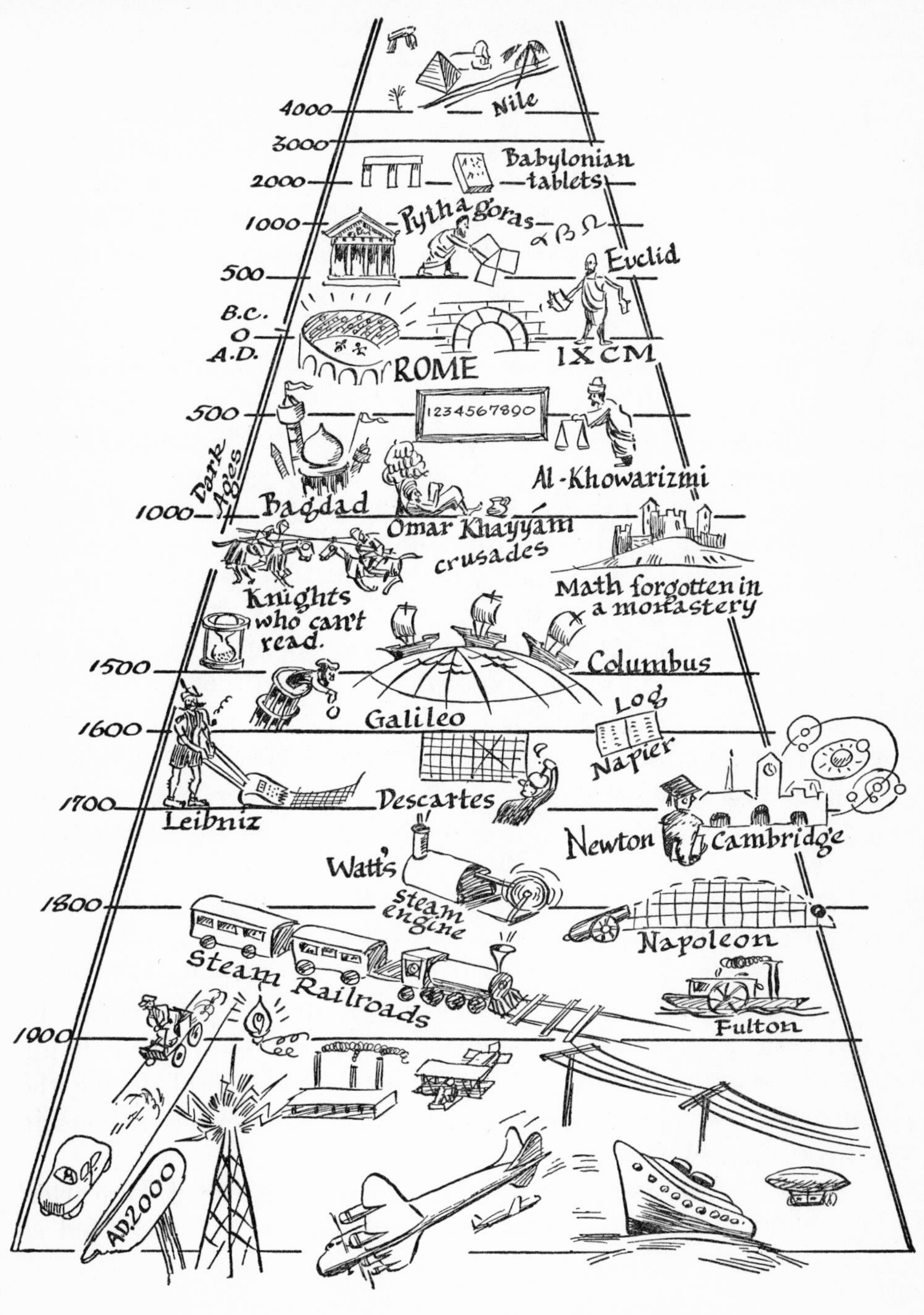
4000
Nile
3000
Babylonian tablets
2000
1000
Pythagoras
α β Ω
500
Euclid
B.C.
0
A.D.
ROME
IXCM
500
1234567890
Dark Ages
Al-Khowarizmi
1000
Bagdad
Omar Khayyám
crusades
Math forgotten in a monastery
Knights who can't read.
1500
Columbus
Galileo
Log
1600
Napier
1700
Descartes
Leibniz
Newton
Cambridge
Watt's steam engine
1800
Napoleon
Steam Railroads
Fulton
1900
A.D. 2000

What a time we had romping through those next two blocks, from 15th Street to 17th Street. There's where we met Newton standing on the shoulders of giants so that he could see the sun, moon, and stars and understand how and why they moved. There's where Leibniz brought out his substitute for the ticking hair clipper and made the error so small that it disappeared entirely when he wanted to measure something which would not stand still. And before that distinguished pair, Newton and Leibniz, what a trio of husky shoulders for all of us to stand on! Descartes, who put Greek geometry and Arab algebra on the checkerboard, crisscrossed with lines full of lies except at one point where lay the truth; Napier with his calculating numbers which let you just add or subtract instead of having to multiply or divide; and Galileo musing under the swaying chandelier in the cathedral or climbing up The Leaning Tower of Pisa with a pendulum and his pockets full of stones.

Back there near 15th Street is Columbus making his way across the Western Ocean into the Unknown. Some of his sailors were sure that they would sail to the rim of the ocean and then just drop off into space. As a mathematician, Columbus didn't amount to much; but he certainly strained every bit of mathematical knowledge he had. For more than two weeks back there in 1492, between November 2 and November 20, he tried to locate his latitude by the stars. He was actually sailing around the northeast shore of Cuba between latitude 21° and 22°, but where do you think his reckoning by the stars told him he was? In latitude 42°.

That would indicate that he was as far north as New York! So he put his instruments and pencil away and went back to dead reckoning. The reason for his mistake was that the pointers in the Dipper had dipped down to the horizon and Columbus probably had picked out another star, Alfirk, instead of Polaris, the North Star, to "shoot" for his position.

Now what do you suppose is the point of including a story about Columbus' scant knowledge of mathematics and worse knowledge of astronomy in a romper's review of mathematics?

It's a very important point, and it doesn't belong in any single chapter, whether it be arithmetic or algebra, or geometry, or trigonometry, or calculus. It belongs in *all* of them. The point is that you must use your hands and feet first in solving any problem in mathematics. Otherwise you may be shooting at Alfirk instead of Polaris. The way to use your feet is to plant them solidly in the middle of the problem and take a good look around. You can form a rough general idea of the answer. You can tell whether the answer is going to be near $1 or $10 or $100 or $1,000. Then you use your hands. Take a firm grasp of what you have to work with. Know what it is that you are going to multiply or divide or add or subtract to get what you want. Then . . . and only then, go to work with your head.

So we look down the road past Columbus into that long barren stretch "When Knighthood Was in Flower." Romantic times, yes; fair maidens, and knights in shining armor charging at each other with lances levelled. But most of them couldn't read or write, let alone calculate with numbers. Learning, including mathematics, in Europe was confined to a few isolated monasteries. A few dusty manuscripts held secrets which even the monks hadn't taken the trouble to discover.

But back along the road between 5th Street and 10th Street, we had romped our way through the Arab part of town. There ahead of the Crusades we had passed Omar Khayyám sitting under the tree with his book of verse on the ground while he figured out the apparently magic numbers which fitted into the binomial theorem. Farther along was Al-Khowarizmi holding his balance pan and filling both sides to keep his equations true. And back of him a century or two we passed that remarkable Arab invention, 1, 2, 3, 4, 5, 6, 7, 8, 9, and *zero.* That was the invention which put to shame all the numbers of the Romans and the Greeks with their I X M CCC VII's and their "alphabet" alpha, beta, gamma, pi, and omega numbers.

You know, I've been thinking quite a bit about the journey

along those two long blocks the other side of the Roman Arch of Triumph. That was where we met Euclid and Pythagoras. I've decided that Pythagoras is the sort of old fellow who grows on you with longer acquaintance. On the other hand, I think Euclid was rather a stuffy type. After all, he wasn't much of a geometer. He just wrote a textbook and other people who preceded him like the discoverers of the Babylonian magic 3-4-5 triangle, and the Egyptian Rope-Swingers, and men like Pythagoras did the creative work.

Still when you say Euclid to nine out of ten people today, his name means "geometry" to them. Certainly, he wrote down the rules, and he drew the illustrations and diagrams for the theorems; he arranged them in neat and orderly fashion, and he passed on the idea that in pure geometry you can't use anything but a ruler and pencil and compass.

But sometimes I wonder whether or not Euclid belongs more in the field of logic rather than in the field of mathematics. After all the average person doesn't see too much importance attached to the definition that a point is "that which has no dimension" and a straight line is "a point moving in one direction." It's quite easy for an ordinary mind to grasp the fact that when you let a plumb line come to rest, its shadow against a board frozen in the ice of a skating rink makes two right angles with the ice. After all, why all this talk about "from a point" or "at a point, a perpendicular and but one can be erected to a line." That sounds like a debating society "line." So my feeling about Euclid is that his books, and all others based on his, should be read through quickly and twice. The first time they should be read through as you would read a picture book about mathematics. After all, it isn't everyone who can see right away how to divide an angle into two equal angles by using merely a compass and ruler. (Men and women have been working a long time trying to divide it into three angles by a simple method without a protractor.) It is quite interesting to see how to draw a circle inside a triangle or outside it. The next time you read Euclid's books, read them as you would the Congressional Record.

Of course, no one reads the Congressional Record; but if you did you might be interested to see how much or how little logic there was in the speech of your senator or representative. Be that as it may, you, Romper, will probably have to go on plodding through Geometry I and Geometry II just to prove to your parents and teachers that you have a mind which is worth a little more cultivation in college.

With Pythagoras, the situation is different. He was a real creative artist. Do you realize what that old gentleman must have gone through during the nights and days he was trying to *prove* that the square of the side opposite the right angle in a triangle was equal to the squares on the two other sides? He knew that it was so; but he had to prove it. Haven't you ever known something was true but couldn't prove it to the other fellow's satisfaction?

That right triangle with its squares is an extremely important factor in the whole development of mathematics. It's more or less to mathematics what the gasoline engine is to the automobile, truck, tractor, motorcycle, speedboat, and aeroplane. In the first place, without the proof for the square of the hypotenuse, there would be no trigonometry and without trigonometry there would be no astronomy. The square of the hypotenuse is basic in Napier's logarithms. One may venture the opinion that without logarithms not only astronomers but also physicists and engineers would work themselves into early graves. Of course it is extremely important to Descartes working at his checkerboard. Isn't Descartes' definition of a circle on his plotting board, $x^2 + y^2 = 1$, or some other number? And we must not forget that Barrow's triangle in differential and integral calculus is only Pythagoras' triangle put to work on a new job. And where would we be in this world of modern wonders without calculus?

Beyond Pythagoras, the road into the past becomes narrower and narrower, dimmer and dimmer. There we passed the Egyptian Rope-Swingers and the Babylonians. Men counted babies and sheep and measured grain and land. They made calendars so that they would know about the seasons of the year but they thought — if they thought about it at all — that the earth was flat and that the sun and stars revolved around the flat earth. They counted on their fingers and toes for many, many centuries and they arranged beads on strings in frames and used the counting frames.

Well, it's taken men and women a long, long time to collect and arrange all the mental tools we have for counting and measuring. As Rompers, we have had an amusing time looking over the exhibits in the museum. We may have seen something which interested us or something which we can use to our advantage. At least, none of the exhibits will be as mysterious as it was or entirely strange any longer.

There is one mistake to be avoided. Having romped through mathematics, none of us is as yet a mathematician. To become a good mathematician, it is necessary to remove one's rompers. A pair of blue jeans rolled half way up to the knees is much more appropriate, now that our romping trip is over, and it might not be a bad idea to roll up the sleeves, too!